Childhood

OF FAMOUS AMERICANS

CHILDHOOD
OF FAMOUS
AMERICANS

INDIANS

BLACK HAWK, *Cleven*
CHIEF JOSEPH, *Burt*
OSCEOLA, *Clark*
POCAHONTAS, *Seymour*
PONTIAC, *Peckham*
SACAGAWEA, *Seymour*
SEQUOYAH, *Snow*
SITTING BULL, *Stevenson*
SQUANTO, *Stevenson*
TECUMSEH, *Stevenson*

NAVAL HEROES

DAVID FARRAGUT, *Long*
GEORGE DEWEY, *Long*
JOHN PAUL JONES, *Snow*
MATTHEW CALBRAITH PERRY, *Scharbach*
OLIVER HAZARD PERRY, *Long*
RAPHAEL SEMMES, *Snow*
STEPHEN DECATUR, *Smith*

NOTED WIVES and MOTHERS

ABIGAIL ADAMS, *Wagoner*
DOLLY MADISON, *Monsell*
ELEANOR ROOSEVELT, *Weil*
JESSIE FREMONT, *Wagoner*
MARTHA WASHINGTON, *Wagoner*
MARY TODD LINCOLN, *Wilkie*
NANCY HANKS, *Stevenson*
RACHEL JACKSON, *Govan*

SCIENTISTS and INVENTORS

ABNER DOUBLEDAY, *Dunham*
ALBERT EINSTEIN, *Hammontree*
ALECK BELL, *Widdemer*
CYRUS McCORMICK, *Dobler*
ELI WHITNEY, *Snow*
ELIAS HOWE, *Corcoran*
ELIZABETH BLACKWELL, *Henry*
GAIL BORDEN, *Paradis*
GEORGE CARVER, *Stevenson*
GEORGE EASTMAN, *Henry*
GEORGE PULLMAN, *Myers*
GEORGE WESTINGHOUSE, *Dunham*
GLENN L. MARTIN, *Harley*
HENRY FORD, *Aird and Ruddiman*
JEAN FELIX PICCARD, *de Grummond and Delaune*
JOHN AUDUBON, *Mason*
JOHN BURROUGHS, *Frisbee*
JOHN DEERE, *Bare*
JOHN FITCH, *Stevenson*
LEE DEFOREST, *Dobler*
LUTHER BURBANK, *Burt*
MARIA MITCHELL, *Melin*
ROBERT FULTON, *Henry*
ROBERT GODDARD, *Moore*
SAMUEL MORSE, *Snow*

TOM EDISON, *Guthridge*
WALTER REED, *Higgins*
WILBUR AND ORVILLE WRIGHT, *Stevenson*
WILL AND CHARLIE MAYO, *Hammontree*

SOCIAL and CIVIC LEADERS

BETSY ROSS, *Weil*
BOOKER T. WASHINGTON, *Stevenson*
CLARA BARTON, *Stevenson*
DAN BEARD, *Mason*
DOROTHEA DIX, *Melin*
FRANCES WILLARD, *Mason*
HELEN KELLER, *Wilkie*
J. STERLING MORTON, *Moore*
JANE ADDAMS, *Wagoner*
JOHN PETER ZENGER, *Long*
JULIA WARD HOWE, *Wagoner*
JULIETTE LOW, *Higgins*
LILIUOKALANI, *Newman*
LUCRETIA MOTT, *Burnett*
MARTIN LUTHER KING, JR., *Millender*
MOLLY PITCHER, *Stevenson*
OLIVER WENDELL HOLMES, JR., *Dunham*
ROBERT TODD LINCOLN, *Anderson*
SUSAN ANTHONY, *Monsell*

SOLDIERS

ALVIN C. YORK, *Weddle*
ANTHONY WAYNE, *Stevenson*
BEDFORD FORREST, *Parks*
DAN MORGAN, *Bryant*
DOUGLAS MacARTHUR, *Long*
ETHAN ALLEN, *Winders*
FRANCIS MARION, *Steele*
GEORGE CUSTER, *Stevenson*
ISRAEL PUTNAM, *Stevenson*
JEB STUART, *Winders*
NATHANAEL GREENE, *Peckham*
ROBERT E. LEE, *Monsell*
SAM HOUSTON, *Stevenson*
TOM JACKSON, *Monsell*
U. S. GRANT, *Stevenson*
WILLIAM HENRY HARRISON, *Peckham*
ZACK TAYLOR, *Wilkie*

STATESMEN

ABE LINCOLN, *Stevenson*
ADLAI STEVENSON, *Ward*
ANDY JACKSON, *Stevenson*
DAN WEBSTER, *Smith*
FRANKLIN ROOSEVELT, *Weil*
HENRY CLAY, *Monsell*
HERBERT HOOVER, *Comfort*
JAMES MONROE, *Widdemer*
JEFF DAVIS, *de Grummond and Delaune*
JOHN F. KENNEDY, *Frisbee*
JOHN MARSHALL, *Monsell*
TEDDY ROOSEVELT, *Parks*
WOODROW WILSON, *Monsell*

Frederic Remington

Young Artist

Illustrated by Robert Doremus

Frederic Remington

Young Artist

By Clyde B. Moore

THE **BOBBS-MERRILL** COMPANY, INC.
A SUBSIDIARY OF HOWARD W. SAMS & CO., INC.
Publishers • INDIANAPOLIS • NEW YORK

LIBRARY OF CONGRESS CATALOG CARD NUMBER: 72-146330

PRINTED IN THE UNITED STATES OF AMERICA

*Dedicated to the boys and girls who express
themselves through sketches, color, and form*

Most helpful in this enterprise has been Atwood Manley, author of a charming brochure, *Frederic Remington: In the Land of His Youth,* prepared for Canton's Remington Centennial Observance. The sections "The Old Home Town" and "Remington's Early Years" were particularly helpful. Best of all were his gracious and generous conversations concerning his personal relationships with Frederic Remington.

Andrew Peters, Librarian for St. Lawrence, with good grace opened a rich collection of Remingtonana in the university.

Available to me were the voluminous bound volumes of *Collier's, Harper's Weekly, Harper's Monthly; History of the North Country* (3 vol.); *History of St. Lawrence County; Frederic Remington: Artist of the Old West* by Harold McCracken (excellent bibliography); *Frederic Remington's Own West* by Remington; *Pony Tracks* by Remington; *Painter of the Wild West* by McKown; *Artists and Illustrators of the Old West* by Taft and others.

Illustrations

Numerous smaller illustrations

Contents

Books by Clyde B. Moore

FREDERIC REMINGTON: YOUNG ARTIST
J. STERLING MORTON: ARBOR DAY BOY
ROBERT GODDARD: PIONEER ROCKET BOY

★ **F**rederic

Remington

Young Artist

Early Childhood Days

Young frederic remington sat looking at a picture of his father. The picture showed his father, Seth Pierre Remington, seated on a horse. "Is this really a picture of my father?" he asked thoughtfully.

"Yes, you may be very proud of your father," said his mother, Clara Remington. "He is an officer in the cavalry of the Union Army, fighting to save his country."

Frederic, whom everybody called Fred, had been born in October, 1861, at Canton, New York, shortly after the beginning of the War between the States. About two months later, his father had taken off to join the cavalry in the Union Army. Then Mrs. Remington and Fred had gone to live with her parents, Mr. and Mrs. Henry L. Sackrider, in Canton.

Now Fred was nearly four years old, but he was too young to understand much about the war. He knew that his father and other men from Canton were away fighting, but he didn't understand where or why. He knew that they fought with cannons, guns, and swords. He knew that people were worried and that every now and then a soldier was injured or killed.

Mrs. Remington handed Fred another picture. This picture showed his father standing between two other officers, holding the hilt of a sword resting upright on the ground beside him. All the officers wore uniforms with brass buttons and emblems on their shoulders. "That's my father in the middle, holding the sword," said Fred. "He surely looks brave standing there."

"Your father is a very brave officer," said Mrs. Remington. "He has helped to win several victories for the Union Army."

Every now and then Fred played that he was a cavalryman like his father. He placed a stick between his legs and dragged it about the house, pretending he was riding a horse. Often he shouted commands, just as he imagined his father did in the army.

Nearly every week Mrs. Remington received a letter from her husband. One day she received a letter which she read over and over again. The letter explained that the Union Army had conquered most of the South. Much of the fighting was now taking place in Virginia, where the Union Army was trying to capture the city of Richmond. Once the Union Army won this important victory, the war would be over.

Fred watched his mother as she read the letter. He wondered why she read it over and over so many times. Finally he said, "Will you read the letter to me, Mama?"

Mrs. Remington read the letter aloud to Fred, but he didn't understand much of what she read. He didn't know where Virginia was, only that it was someplace far away. The only thing he understood was that the war might soon be over. "Will Father come home?" he asked.

"Probably not for weeks or months," replied Mrs. Remington. "He is a gallant leader and won't come home until the Union Army wins. We won't see him until the war is over."

Fred was pleased with what his mother said. He could tell that she was proud of his father and wanted him to stay as long as he would be needed. He was proud of his father, too.

Fred enjoyed living with Grandfather and Grandmother Sackrider. He and his grandfather became great pals. Every day they spent many hours going places and doing things together. Mr. Sackrider, who was called Deacon Sackrider because of his work in the church, had many friends in and around Canton.

Every few days Fred and his mother went to visit his other grandparents, Mr. and Mrs. Samuel N. Remington, who also lived in Canton. His grandfather, who was known as Reverend Remington, was a preacher in one of the churches in Canton. Always he and Grandmother Remington read and talked about letters which they had received from Fred's father.

Grandfather and Grandmother Sackrider lived next to the St. Lawrence County Fairground in Canton. There were stables and a racetrack in the fairground, where race horses were kept and trained. Each day during the summer when the weather was good, trainers would bring their horses out on the track to practice. Then during the fair, which would be held early in the fall, real races would be held.

Nearly every day during the summer Grand-father Sackrider took Fred to watch the horses and trainers. They stood behind a fence where they could watch without getting in the way. Sometimes when the trainers were working in the stables, they invited Grandfather and Fred to come inside. They talked with Fred and told him many things about the horses.

Fred liked to watch the trainers groom the horses inside the stables. First they combed the horses' coats with a metal comb, called a curry-comb, to loosen dirt. Then they brushed the coats with a long brush to make the hair look bright and clean.

The men took special care of the horses' manes and tails. They combed and brushed the long hairs over and over again. When they finished, every hair seemed to hang and stay in exactly the right place.

Afterwards the trainers took the horses out-

16

side to exercise on the track. They rode some of the horses and drove others hitched to two-wheeled carts called sulkies. Round and round the track they went with the horses holding their heads high in the air.

Sometimes when Grandfather Sackrider was busy, Fred watched the trainers and horses by himself. Then he usually climbed on a high stump near the fence, where he could look out over the track. Always he was warned never to go inside the fairground by himself.

Over a century ago, when Fred was a small boy, horses were numerous and important animals. Farmers used horses for pulling farm machinery in the fields and for pulling wagons and carriages on county roads. City and town people used horses to pull wagons and drays and carriages on the streets. Also people in both city and country used horses for riding.

Horses were of many sizes and colors. Some

were large and slow-moving, good for pulling heavy loads. Others were thinner and speedier, good for riding and for driving hitched to carriages, such as buggies, carts, and surreys. Horses were white, black, gray, tan, sorrel, or of varied colors, as dappled and spotted.

Many people owned horses. Farmers always had several horses, and people in cities and towns often kept a horse or two. In those days there were no tractors to pull farm machinery and no automobiles, buses, or trucks to travel along highways and streets. There were a few railroads, but no airplanes, so people had to depend largely on horses for transportation.

Grandfather Sackrider owned a horse named Kitty that was good for both riding horseback and driving hitched to a carriage. Fred often watched Grandfather curry and brush Kitty's bay coat and hitch her to a buggy to go for a ride. Sometimes Grandfather let Fred hold the lines to pretend that he was driving. Then Fred felt very important, almost grown up.

One morning after Grandfather had finished grooming Kitty he put a bridle on her and led her from the stable. Outside he called to Fred, who was standing nearby watching, "Come and take a ride on Kitty."

"Oh, thank you, Grandfather!" said Fred, coming on the run.

Grandfather picked Fred up and placed him on Kitty's back. He gave Fred the reins but held on to the bridle with one hand. Then he led Kitty slowly around and around the yard. Fred was thrilled. At last he was riding a horse! Now he knew how the trainers felt when they rode horses around the racetrack.

Fred learned many thing about horses from watching Kitty. He noticed how she held her head and how she lifted her front feet when she walked or trotted. He noticed that she never

19

got her hind feet tangled up with her front feet. Sometimes he got down on his hands and feet and pretended that he was Kitty to see whether he could walk or trot as she did.

He was curious about Kitty's shoes. "Why does she have to wear shoes?" he asked.

"To protect her feet," replied Grandfather. "The shoes keep her from breaking off the edges of her hoofs and from bruising the tender center parts of her hoofs."

"Does it hurt her to have the shoes nailed on?" asked Fred.

"No, the edges of her hoofs are very hard and have no feeling in them," said Grandfather. "She doesn't feel the nails when the blacksmith puts on the shoes."

"May I go to the blacksmith shop the next time you take Kitty to get new shoes?" asked Fred. "I'll stay out of the way."

"Yes, to be sure," said Grandfather. "Maybe

we can go tomorrow. Kitty's shoes are becoming worn and she needs new ones."

Up to now Grandfather had avoided taking Fred to the blacksmith shop, because it was a dangerous place for children. Horses were always coming and going, and many of them were nervous about being shod. Besides, there always was danger from fiery sparks flying about.

The next morning Grandfather went to the stable to get Kitty ready for the trip to the blacksmith shop. First he went over her body with a currycomb and brush to make her coat look neat and clean. Next he placed the harness on her body and hitched her to the buggy. Then he helped Fred climb up to the seat in the buggy and climbed up beside him.

Off they went to the blacksmith shop to get some new shoes for Kitty. On the way Fred asked Grandfather several questions about

Kitty and her new shoes. He wondered how she felt about going to the blacksmith shop. Did she know she would get some new shoes?

When they reached the blacksmith shop, Grandfather unhitched Kitty, took off her harness, and led her inside. The blacksmith came over, spoke to her quietly, patted her gently, and rubbed her well-groomed coat. He seemed to know just what to do and wore a big leather apron to protect himself.

The blacksmith took time to show Fred about the shop. He showed him the fire in the forge where he heated metal to make it red-hot. He pulled a rod that caused a big bag-like device, called a bellows, to force air through the fire and make it glow. He pointed out a big iron block, called an anvil, on which he hammered hot pieces of iron.

After showing Fred the shop, the blacksmith went back to Kitty. Once more he spoke to her gently and patted her. First he lifted each of her feet and pried off the old shoe with a tool called tongs. Then he clipped off ragged portions of the hoof with sharp pinchers and smoothed the bottom with a big file, called a rasp. In this way he made each hoof ready for a new shoe.

Finally the blacksmith walked over to a big rack of new horseshoes to pick out some new shoes for Kitty. Some of the shoes were large and heavy, good for big workhorses that pulled heavy loads. Other shoes were small and light, good for carriage and riding horses such as Kitty. In each case the shoes had to be fitted to a horse's hoofs, much as shoes are fitted to a person's feet.

After the blacksmith found the right shoes for Kitty, he thrust each shoe into the forge to heat it. He pumped the bellows for a moment to make the fire in the forge become red-hot. Then he pulled the red-hot shoe from the fire

with a pair of tongs, placed it on the anvil, and
hammered it into proper shape.

The blacksmith tried each shoe on one of Kitty's hoofs to be sure it would fit perfectly. If he

24

was satisfied, he nailed the shoe in place on the hoof and cut off the ends of the nails. Finally he checked to make certain the nails held the shoe securely against the hoof.

When the blacksmith finished shoeing Kitty, Grandfather led her from the blacksmith shop, put on her harness, and hitched her again to the carriage. On the way home she held her head high, as if she were very proud. "She must like her new shoes," said Fred.

"Yes," said Grandfather. "She feels more sure-footed in walking and trotting."

"Thank you for taking me with you," said Fred. "I had fun at the blacksmith shop."

That evening Fred played that he was a black-smith shoeing a horse. He used a kitchen chair for a horse and pretended that each leg of the chair was a horse's leg. Then he went from leg to leg to fasten a shoe on the hoof.

Pictures and Horses

ONE NIGHT in late summer it rained very hard in Canton. In the morning Fred looked out his window and saw puddles of water standing here and there in the yard. He was disappointed, because he knew he would have to stay indoors while the ground was still wet.

By now the county fair was only a few weeks away, and each day the trainers drove and rode their horses around the racetrack. This forenoon Fred had hoped to watch the trainers ride and drive the horses, but now the track was muddy and not a trainer or horse was in sight. Fred knew there would be no practice today.

Fred ate his breakfast quietly, but Grand-mother Sackrider could see that he was greatly disappointed. "I'm sorry," she said in her kindly manner, "that you won't get to watch the horses today. Now we'll have to plan something for you to do inside the house. I have a pleasant surprise for you, but you'll have to wait until I clear the table."

"A surprise!" cried Fred, looking up eagerly. "What kind of a surprise?"

"I can't tell you," said Grandmother, "or it wouldn't be a surprise. Just wait until I finish clearing the table."

Fred waited patiently while Grandmother fin-ished clearing the table, all the while wonder-ing what the surprise could be. Finally she placed a big box on the table. "Here is the sur-prise," she said as she took a few pictures from the box.

Grandmother had purchased the pictures to

help entertain people in her home. They had been printed by a company that specialized in collecting and selling interesting pictures. Some of them were printed in beautiful colors and others in black and white.

Fred was astonished as he began to look at the pictures to find a number of pictures of horses. He decided to sort out these pictures and look at them first. Each picture had a printed title, which Grandmother read to him.

The first picture, which was caller *Alexander*, showed a man standing beside a horse. Fred shook his head in disappointment. Even at his young age, he was a good judge of horses. "That horse couldn't race," he said. "His legs are too short. Let me see a horse racing."

Grandmother pulled out a picture called *Flora Temple*, which showed a horse trotting at full speed on a racetrack. Fred's eyes sparkled with delight as he looked at the picture of this horse. Here was a horse in action, the kind of horse that he liked to see.

As he continued to look at the picture, once more he shook his head. He noticed that the horse was hitched to a four-wheeled vehicle, somewhat like a buggy without a top. "That's not a sulky," he said. "It's not good for racing."

Next Grandmother pulled out a picture called *A Head and Head Finish*, which showed eight horses running neck to neck in a race. Fred enjoyed this picture, because it showed a real race in which any of the horses could win. He was more pleased with this picture than any he had seen yet. "I wish I could tell which horse will win," he said.

Soon they came to a picture called *Dutchman*, which showed a horse with a short tail. "Oh, Grandmother," said Fred, "look at the short tail on this horse."

"Yes," said Grandmother, "the horse's tail has

been docked. That means that it has been cut off to shorten it for some reason."

"Cut off!" cried Fred. "What a mean way to treat a horse!"

The next picture, called *Trotting Cracks at the Forge*, showed two handsome bay horses in a blacksmith shop. This picture showed a fancy blacksmith shop with pictures hanging on the walls and a shelf covered with ornaments. Once again Fred shook his head. "This is not a real blacksmith shop," he said. "There are no pictures in a real blacksmith shop."

Another picture, called *Trotting Races on the Snow*, showed a winter scene with horses drawing light cutters or sleighs. Fred enjoyed this picture because the winter before he had taken a ride in a sleigh with Grandfather Sackrider. He remembered how smoothly the sleigh had slipped along over the snowy streets.

The final picture, which was called *George M.*

Patchen, Brown Dick, and Miller's Damsel, showed three horses in a trotting race. Each horse was hitched to a light sulky with very high wheels. "This is a good picture," said Fred. "These are good trotting horses and the sulkies are just like some of the sulkies here on the race-track at the fairground."

Fred had a wonderful time looking at Grandmother's pictures. Partly he enjoyed looking at them just because they were pictures of horses. Also he was pleased because he could point out weaknesses in some of the pictures.

"Grandmother, I want to draw a horse," he said. "Let me try to draw a horse."

Grandmother got Fred a sheet of paper and a pencil. Then he copied one of the horses trotting in the last picture. His drawing was crude, but it looked like a real horse. "You are a good artist," said Grandmother. "We must show your drawing to Grandfather."

31

Grandfather was greatly pleased with the picture. "Why, you're only four years old, but you can draw better than I can," he said. "We must save your picture to show people when they come to visit us."

The following morning the sky was clear and Fred awakened to find sunshine bursting into his room. He bounced out of bed, eager to spend much of the day outdoors. Perhaps he and Grandfather could watch the trainers practice their horses on the racetrack at the fairground.

"The sun is shining today," said Fred as he entered the kitchen. "May we go to watch the horses practice on the racetrack?"

"Yes, but eat a good breakfast," replied Grandfather. "Then we'll go out to watch."

Fred hurried through his breakfast of scrambled eggs, sweet rolls, butter, jam, and a large glass of milk. "Well, I'm ready," he said, looking over at Grandfather, who was still busy eat-

33

ing. "I'll go out to the stump and start to watch, if I may."

"How fast he is growing up," Grandmother said to Grandfather. "He already is large for his age, one of the sturdiest boys I have ever seen. And he certainly is crazy about horses!"

"Someday he should make a great horseman," replied Grandfather.

Outside, Fred made his way to a tree stump near the racetrack. Already the trainers were busy grooming and exercising the horses. This would be a great day to watch.

In a few minutes Grandfather went out to join Fred. Shortly one of the trainers, named George Driver, noticed them watching by the fence and invited them to come inside to the stables. Immediately they started for the gate that opened into the fairground.

When they reached the stables, they found Mr. Driver grooming a beautiful three-year-old black mare. First he combed her coat to make it clean and shiny. Next he examined her hoofs to make sure that her shoes fit tight and no pebbles were lodged in the soft portions of her feet. "I'm going to drive her hitched to a new sulky," he said.

Mr. Driver showed Grandfather and Fred the new sulky which he had just purchased. It had bright red wheels about as high as Fred's head. It was made of light materials and was supposed to be easy to pull.

Grandfather stepped up to the sulky and lifted one of the wheels off the ground. "Why, it's almost as light as a feather," he said. "Is it strong enough to stand up in a race?"

"Oh, yes," replied Mr. Driver. "Even though it is light, it is really very sturdy. The manufacturer guarantees it, except for a clash with another sulky."

Soon Mr. Driver put some harness on the

black mare and hitched her to the new sulky. He climbed up on the seat of the sulky and started to drive away. By now several other trainers were on the track with their horses. Before long they would have some kind of a practice race. Grandfather and Fred went back to their yard to watch through the fence.

First each driver would test his horse's gait, or normal speed of trotting or pacing. He would watch the horse's foot movements to see whether they were steady. He would note whether the horse's leg muscles seemed to be strong and well-seasoned, with plenty of flexibility.

When a driver found that his horse was trotting or pacing with an even rhythm, he would urge the horse to travel a little faster. The purpose of the exercise was to find the fastest possible gait for the horse, then have the horse practice this gait day after day.

Fred watched for Mr. Driver and his new

sulky with shiny red wheels. Soon he went dashing by with reins and whip in hand, driving the beautiful three-year-old black mare. The mare was stepping along at a lively gait and looked like a sure winner later on. She was one of the best horses at the track.

"How beautiful and graceful she is," thought Fred. "She moves as fast as the wind and her feet scarcely touch the ground. What fun it must be to drive her."

Beginning School Days

AFTER THE War between the States ended, Fred's father, Seth Pierre Remington, returned home to join his family. He had been promoted to Colonel and everybody now called him Colonel Remington. He and Mrs. Remington and Fred moved into a home of their own.

Colonel Remington bought and edited a newspaper in Canton, known as the *Plaindealer*. This newspaper, which was published once a week, was read both by the people of Canton and by the people of St. Lawrence County. It was printed in a large building near the center of town, called the Union Block Building.

Fred was very proud of his father as a newspaper man. Every few days he dropped in at the *Plaindealer* office to see his father and to watch men setting type and running the printing presses. By now he was old enough to know that reading was very important.

As Fred became older his mother taught him beginning reading and arithmetic. Finally one September morning he was old enough to start to school. He left home alone but soon caught up with other children. All were neatly dressed and many wore new clothes.

Fred enjoyed walking along the street with the other children. He was a sociable boy who liked to be with people. At first he wasn't sure whether or not he wanted to start school, but joining these other children gave him courage and made him feel happier.

As a schoolboy Fred looked little like a beginner. He was large for his age, larger than some children who had gone to school for two or three years. The other children could hardly believe that he was only a beginner.

At the school building, the children scattered. Some went to one room and some to another. Fred went to the room for beginners. The teacher, Miss Whitney, sat at a desk on a platform at the front of the room. She was making a record of the children, taking their names and assigning them seats. "What is your name?" she asked when Fred reached her desk.

"Frederic," replied Fred.

"Can you spell it for me?" she asked, partly to find out whether Fred could spell.

"F-r-e-d-e-r-i-c," replied Fred. Then he added, "No 'k' at the end."

"Thank you," said Miss Whitney. "I am glad you helped me with the spelling. In another second I might have written your name with a 'k'. Your last name is Remington, isn't it?"

"Yes, ma'am," Fred replied proudly. "I am Colonel Remington's son."

"How old are you?" asked Miss Whitney.

"Six," replied Fred, "but I'll have a birthday next month."

"My, you are big for your age," said Miss Whitney. "Your mother must be a good cook."

"She certainly is," said Fred, smiling, "and I like to eat."

Fred shrugged his shoulders and winked at the freckle-faced, red-haired boy who was next in line. Miss Whitney looked at this boy. "What is your name?" she asked.

"Michael, but everybody calls me Mike," the boy replied. "My father's name is the same, Michael Murphy, but people call him Big Mike. They call me Little Mike."

Miss Whitney took a sharp look at these two friendly boys. At once she decided to assign them to seats in different parts of the room.

Otherwise, she thought, two boys as lively-looking as these might cause trouble.

All the desks in the room were wide enough for two children, so the children had to sit together in pairs. Miss Whitney assigned Michael to a desk near the front of the room and Fred to a desk near the back. The desks in the back of the room were larger than those near the front of the room.

Miss Whitney believed in strict discipline. She gave her pupils orders as if they were a company of soldiers. When she called the arithmetic class to recite, she anounced, "Arithmetic class, attention!" Then she followed with "One," which meant for the pupils to take up their books, and "Two," which meant for them to stand beside their desks, and "Three," which meant for them to march to the recitation bench at the front of the room.

Fred could do his work well, but he had many

interests besides books. He greatly enjoyed the recess periods when the children went outdoors to run and play in the school yard. He enjoyed wrestling and could outwrestle any boy of his age in the school.

There were few textbooks in the school. Most of the textbooks were passed along from one pupil to another for several years. Each pupil managed to write a few rhyming wisecracks in the book. Fred enjoyed reading all the rhymes which others had written.

Here are some rhymes that he found:

If this book should roam
Box its ears and send it home.

Steal not this book for fear of strike
For the owner carries a big jackknife.

If my name you wish to see
Look on page 73.

If my name you cannot find
Shut the book and never mind.

If there should be another flood,
Then to this book I'd fly;
If all the earth should be submerged
This book would still be dry.

In those days children were supposed to study their books and not to waste time drawing pictures. Fred found it hard to obey these directions. He opened his books and pretended to study but spent much time making sketches in the margins. Ever since he could remember, he had liked to draw, but this was the first time he had spent much time at drawing.

As thousands of other pupils have done, he often drew pictures of his teacher, but they were not intended to be funny. He observed Miss Whitney carefully and tried to make his drawings of her real. How did she dress? What kind of shoes did she wear? How did she comb her hair?

All these things were important, but Fred even observed more closely. How did Miss Whitney act? How did she sit at her desk? How did she stand? How did she walk? How did she use her hands? How did she hold a ruler? All these things needed to go into the sketches, too.

Fred's drawings of Miss Whitney seemed to come alive. They showed her as she really looked and acted in the schoolroom. Obviously some of them were not very flattering, even though they were realistic. Therefore Fred always tried to keep most of them hidden.

Besides making sketches of Miss Whitney, Fred made many other sketches in school. He got many ideas for drawing from his textbooks and drew sketches of horses, soldiers, hunters, trappers, and Indians. Drawing became a habit with him. Whenever he saw a piece of paper or an open place in a book, somehow it seemed to say, "Draw a picture here."

Neither Miss Whitney nor Fred's parents approved of his interest in drawing. They had read articles about artists failing to make a living and gave him little encouragement. Miss Whitney said that he was intelligent and wanted him to become a good student. His parents felt that his large size would help him to become a successful businessman. They wanted him to become a good student, too.

Fred was very critical of the pictures which he found in his textbooks. He thought that many of them were poorly done, particularly pictures of horses. They were stilted and showed the horses standing as if they were made of stone. Real horses usually were in motion.

Even though Fred received little encouragement for his interest in drawing, he decided to keep on sketching. More and more he drew sketches of horses to show horses as they really were, prancing, galloping, and running. He began to study the actions of horses with great care. How did they hold their heads? How did they

46

use their feet and legs? How did they bend their front legs and their hind legs?

One day when Fred was making a sketch of a galloping horse, his friend Mike looked over his shoulder. "Why not draw a picture of me on the run?" he suggested. "See whether you can draw me as well as a horse."

Fred looked outside and noticed a dog in the yard. "All right," he said. "Get out there and chase that dog."

Mike ran outside and dashed off like a sky-rocket to catch the dog, but the dog was hard to catch. Mike had to turn this way and that to follow the dog in and out of bushes. All the while Fred studied Mike's movements. He noted that Mike's right leg was nearly straight and that his left leg was off the ground when he made a quick left turn. The reverse was true when he made a quick right turn.

The young artist caught the meaning of Mike's

varied movements. Mike straightened one leg to help him stop running in one direction and he lifted his other leg to help him swing his body in making a turn.

Fred carefully drew Mike's legs in the correct positions. Soon Mike came to look at the sketch over Fred's shoulder. "Gee!" he exclaimed. "That really looks like me."

The next day was Saturday. Fred went to Grandfather Sackrider's home to watch the horses at the fairground. He made several sketches of the horses, showing them in action. On Monday morning when he returned to school, he showed some of the sketches to Mike. "Let me look at the sketches more closely," said Mike. "Boy, you really are good."

Fred said nothing, but he was greatly pleased by Mike's comment. It was encouraging to know that someone liked his drawings, even though his family and Miss Whitney did not.

The Great Fire

IN THE SUMMER of 1869, when Fred was eight years old, he and his friends spent many hours sauntering in the woods outside Canton. There were several streams nearby where they could fish and swim. Often they took lunches with them and spent complete days in the woods.

One late afternoon in August Fred returned home after spending the day with four other boys in the woods. He was completely exhausted and dropped into a kitchen chair while his mother prepared supper. "I'm tired," he said. "I'm almost too tired to eat."

His mother glanced over to make sure that he

was all right. "What have you been doing to make you so tired?" she asked.

"Everything," replied Fred. "We swam for a while and ate our lunch by a stream. Then this afternoon we pretended that we were Indians walking along a trail. We went farther in the woods than we have ever gone before."

Mrs. Remington looked fondly at Fred and said, "Well, you've had a hard day, but sauntering in the woods is good for you. After you eat supper and get a good night's rest you'll feel all right again."

Fred smiled faintly. Already he was beginning to feel better just from sitting there and inhaling the fragrant odors of food. "I think you're right, Mother," he said. "Nothing can compare with smelling sweet food in your kitchen. Already I'm beginning to feel hungry."

Soon supper was ready and Mrs. Remington called Colonel Remington, who was in the living room reading. The three of them sat down at the table and Colonel Remington asked Fred several questions about his day in the woods. By this time Fred was so busy eating that he could scarcely take time to answer.

"Did you see any real Indians in the woods?" asked Colonel Remington.

"No," replied Fred, "but we pretended that some of us were Indians. We made a wigwam out of sticks and bark from old trees and we hunted with bows and arrows."

Finally it came time for dessert, which consisted of peach shortcake and whipped cream. Fred crammed large chunks of the flaky shortcake into his mouth as if he hadn't eaten for days. "Mother," he said, "this is the best shortcake I've ever tasted."

Mrs. Remington smiled approvingly at this remark from her robust son, who a half hour earlier had been too tired to eat. Then she said,

"Now go on upstairs and get a good night's sleep. Tomorrow you'll feel much better."

Fred told his father and mother good night and trudged slowly up the stairs. In minutes, perhaps seconds, after he went to bed he was sound asleep, lost to the world.

Suddenly he was awakened by the clanging of bells. Church bells, school bells, all the bells in Canton seemed to be ringing. He sprang from bed and ran to the window to find out what was happening. Then he heard wild shouts from the street. "Fire! Fire! Fire!"

"Fred!" his father called. "There's a big fire in town! Come quickly if you want to go with me. I'm going to help fight the fire, but you can go along to watch."

Fred jumped into his clothes and hastened to join his father. In his excitement he completely forgot how tired he had been when he had gone to bed the evening before. Now in the early morning he sprinted beside his father like a runner doing the hundred yard dash.

By now the whole sky glowed a fiery red as long flames leaped upward, turning the night into day. People were rushing from their houses into the streets, eager to find out what was burning. Many were hurrying to see the fire, even mothers with small children. One woman hobbled along with crutches and another pushed herself along in a wheel chair.

"The fire is in the Union Block Building!" somebody cried as Colonel Remington and Fred neared the scene of the fire. Fred was shocked, because the *Plaindealer* offices and plant were located in this building. Already great clouds of black smoke were pouring from the *Plaindealer* windows.

"You stay here, Fred, but be careful. I'm going to help the bucket brigade fight the fire," said Colonel Remington. He was captain of the village bucket brigade and the other members would be coming on the run.

At first Fred could only stand staring and thinking. He knew his father's office and printing plant almost as well as he knew his own home. He knew where the men worked to set type and to run the printing presses. Now everything was being destroyed. He felt sorry for his father and wondered how he could help.

Many times he had heard his father explain how the bucket brigade worked to put out a fire or to keep a fire from spreading. Colonel Remington had organized the bucket brigade because there was no fire department in Canton. Little did he dream that the brigade might fight a fire in his own printing plant.

In those times a bucket brigade was the usual method of fighting fires in small communities. Buckets filled with water were kept in stores and offices ready for dousing out fires the moment they started. Fred had noticed many buckets of water located here and there in the Union Block Building, ready to be used. Now he knew why they were important.

Unfortunately, the fire in the Union Block Building had started at three o'clock in the morning when most people were sound asleep in their beds. There were no people in the building to use the buckets of water. Already the fire had destroyed the printing plant and several offices and shops in the building. Now all the bucket brigade could do was to try to keep the fire from spreading.

The brigade quickly formed two lines to fight the fire. One line passed along buckets filled with water to throw on the flames. The other line passed the empty buckets back to be filled with water again. Colonel Remington moved along the lines, shouting orders much as he had done in battle years before.

Fred moved over to where the brigade was working. At once he felt he could help and jumped into line to help pass buckets of water toward the fire. He was only a boy, but he passed the buckets along as well as the men. Never once did he falter or give up.

On through the night the brigade fought to head off the fire. In the meantime the flames destroyed floors, stairways, rafters, sills, and other supporting timbers. When morning came, little was left of the building or its contents.

This fire was one of the greatest disasters in the history of Canton. The office and printing plant of the *Plaindealer* and several other places of business were destroyed. Colonel Remington managed to save some records, but otherwise he suffered a complete loss.

The next morning, after long hours of fighting flames and dodging collapsing timbers, Colonel Remington and Fred, blackened by smoke, walked slowly homeward. "Fred," said the Colonel, "I'm very proud of you. You're only eight years old, but you worked as well as any man tonight."

Fred was pleased by this comment. Ever since his father had returned from the war, Fred had regarded him as a hero. Now he had seen his father in action and was very proud of him. Furthermore, he was pleased to have had an opportunity to serve under his father, and to hear his father's words of approval.

During the next few weeks Colonel Remington made arrangements to rebuild the *Plaindealer* office and plant in a new location. Also he decided that Canton should have a better way of fighting fires. He planned to put on a campaign to get the people of Canton to organize a real fire department and to purchase a handpumper for fighting fires.

Thus the great fire in Canton led to important improvements. Colonel Remington built a new home for his newspaper and Canton obtained a new fire department.

Exciting Days in Canton

ALL THROUGH the summer the people of Canton and St. Lawrence County looked forward to the St. Lawrence County Fair. This fair, which was the leading event of the year, would be held near the middle of September. On the first day of the fair there would be a big parade in Canton. Men, women, and children from Canton and the country outside would gather along the streets to watch the parade.

Each week Colonel Remington included stories about the fair and parade in the *Plaindealer*. Nearly every evening as Fred and his parents sat eating supper, they talked about things that

60

would happen. Fred was excited and could hardly wait for the fair to come.

One day in August Fred and his friend Pete went for a walk through the business section of Canton. They noticed a mammoth new sign-board on one of the corners. "Oh, look!" cried Fred excitedly. "There's a big new sign about the fair and the parade."

Across the top of the sign in large black letters were the following announcements:

ST. LAWRENCE COUNTY FAIR
SEPTEMBER 17, 18, AND 19
CANTON STREET PARADE
SEPTEMBER 17

"Those dates are only a little more than a month away," said Fred. "This already is almost the middle of August."

"Yes," replied Pete. "Let's go closer to read all the fine print on the sign. The fine print tells what is going to happen."

The boys moved closer and started to read the big sign word by word. They had trouble reading some of the longer words but managed to get most of the meaning. One word which they found hard to make out was the word "Agricultural" in the sentence "On these dates the St. Lawrence Agricultural Society will hold its eighteenth annual fair."

"Why, here's your father's name on the sign," said Pete, pointing upward. "The sign says that Colonel Seth Pierre Remington will lead the parade and that it will start from the center of town at 9:00 o'clock in the forenoon."

"I'll bet he'll ride a horse," said Fred. "He wouldn't be happy without a horse."

One part of the sign told about the horse races to be held during the fair. There would be races with men riding horses and races with men driving horses hitched to sulkies. Cash prizes would be given. "I surely want to see those horse races," said Fred. "They'll be the best part of the fair in my opinion."

The rest of the sign told about the exhibits to be held at the fair. There would be several exhibits of horses, including work horses, carriage horses, and riding horses. "I'll want to draw some of those horses," said Fred.

There would be exhibits of such farm animals as cattle, hogs, sheep, and poultry, and such animal products as wool and eggs. There would be exhibits of farm crops, fruits, and vegetables, including wheat, corn, hops, apples, pears, peaches, potatoes, beets, parsnips, cabbages, turnips, and pumpkins.

There would be exhibits of interest to women, including such articles as quilts, rugs, table cloths, and window curtains. There would be exhibits of baked foods such as bread, cakes, pies, and cookies, and many canned foods, such as canned fruits and vegetables.

One announcement of exhibits seemed very amusing to the boys. It said that there would be an exhibit of oxen and that a premium would be given for the best yoke of oxen over four years old. "I certainly don't want to miss this exhibit," said Pete.

Besides the big sign, there were several smaller signs at business places in Canton. One sign in front of a hotel read:

THE FORREST HOTEL
BOARD AND LODGING $1.00 PER DAY
DURING THE FAIR
HORSES 20 CENTS PER DAY (HAY AND GRAIN EXTRA)

From that time on all the townspeople began to prepare for the fair and the parade. Many repaired and repainted their houses and the fences around their yards. They mowed the yards and cut down weeds in the gardens. They wanted everything in town to look good for visitors when they came in from the country.

64

In the business section of the town merchants repainted the fronts of their stores and shops. Workmen repaired all the streets and sidewalks in the business section and on the way to the fairground. They wanted them to be in good shape for the visitors to use.

One of the busiest spots in town was the fairground. Workmen cut weeds and cleaned away all the trash. They replaced rotten timbers and repaired leaky roofs and broken windows. They spread gallons of fresh paint on old buildings to make them look new.

The workmen gave special attention to the racetrack, which they carefully graded. They tried to make the quarter stretches or sides of the oval track perfectly level so that the horses could run at full speed. Then they carefully shaped the track at the ends of the oval to help them in turning.

At last the week of the fair came. On Monday

and Tuesday dozens of people arrived to set up their exhibits. All wanted their exhibits to look attractive in order to win premiums or awards. Judges would inspect all the exhibits to give out ribbons on everything from corn, tomatoes, peaches, and quilts to cows, sheep, colts, and turkeys.

Would everything be ready for the opening on Wednesday? Would all the ribbons be in place with blue for first place, red for second place, and white for third place? Would all the horses be ready to race at the right moment?

Fred decided to go to bed early on Tuesday night. He wanted to be ready to leap out of bed early the next morning. Then he could take off to watch preparations for the parade.

The next morning he awoke to find sunshine pouring through the window. In seconds he hopped out of bed, dressed, and rushed downstairs to breakfast. While he was waiting for his

66

mother to put the food on the table, he looked at the last issue of the *Plaindealer,* which told about the parade and the program at the fair.

All men who had served in the War between the States were invited to wear their uniforms and to march in the parade. The people of Canton and St. Lawrence County were very proud of the men who had enlisted for military service. Now, since the war was over, they were eager to honor these men whenever possible.

When Fred and his friends arrived to watch preparations for the parade, they found the street crowded with people. Already the Canton Brass Band and several veterans in uniform had assembled to take their places in the parade. In a few minutes Colonel Remington, who was to lead the parade, came riding up on a prancing black charger. Immediately the crowd broke into a tremendous cheer.

Four years of riding in a famous cavalry regi-

ment had given the Colonel remarkable skill as a horseman. Four years of brave fighting at the front had caused him to be regarded as a hero. Now that he had returned home, his friends and neighbors were eager to honor him as a distinguished citizen and leader.

Every brass button and every inch of gold braid on his uniform glistened in the bright sunshine. Many decorations which he had won for meritorious service flashed across his chest. The silver leaves on his shoulders revealed his high rank as an officer. Truly he looked the part of a distinguished leader.

Fred watched his father closely from the side of the crowded street. Proudly he thought, "What a wonderful figure he is, sitting erect on that handsome horse!"

The boys moved on to look at the Canton Brass Band. The members of the band, wearing bright blue uniforms and holding their instruments, waited for a signal from Colonel Remington to start the parade. On the ground rested a big bass drum with the words "Canton Brass Band" lettered on one side.

All the instruments had been polished until they shone like new. The trumpets and other small horns sparkled at the front. The slide trombones and the big bass horn flashed brightly at the rear. All the players were eager to toot their very best.

The boys, watching from the sidewalk, could hardly wait for the parade to start. They wanted to hear the sharp shrill notes of the trumpets and the ump-pa-um-pa-pa of the big bass horn. They wanted to hear the beat of the drums to keep time for marching feet.

Finally police cleared the street and everything was quiet. Old Glory waved gracefully and proudly from a nearby flagpole. Hundreds of people waited on the sidewalks and others leaned out the windows of buildings. Finally Colonel Remington, mounted on his black steed, issued the command, "Forward, march!"

There was a roll of drums. Clear shrill notes came from the trumpets. The other instruments joined in to the beat of the drums. Cheers rang out from the crowd as the persons marching in the parade kept time to the music.

Colonel Remington waited on his steed to ride at the head of the war veterans. The veterans, organized into companies, fell in line, one company after another. They made a colorful sight, dressed in blue uniforms and stepping in unison to the music.

The band marched from the center of town to the entrance of the fairground. People followed the parade, walking along the street. Now the fair was officially opened and people began to go through the gates. Fred and his friends were among the first persons to enter.

The St. Lawrence County Fair

AFTER FRED and his friends entered the fairground, they immediately went to the horse exhibits. These were popular exhibits at the fair, because horses were widely used for carrying on work, transportation, and communication. There still were no automobiles, buses, trucks, or tractors for people to use.

In the case of an accident, someone had to ride horseback to call a doctor. The doctor in turn had to travel to the scene of the accident by horseback or horse and buggy, often over a dusty or muddy road. There were no faster ways of communicating or traveling about.

72

Fred and his friends obtained a printed list of the classifications of horses to guide them in looking about. First they came to the exhibit of mares with colts. The mothers were very attentive to their colts, as if to assure them of protection. The colts were very timid and kept close to their mothers' sides.

The next exhibit included only mares without colts. All the mares seemed calm and gentle and paid little attention to persons who kept coming and going. "These mares really act like ladies," sair Fred.

How different were the stallions! They neighed loudly, pawed the earth, and seemed to resent being tied to posts or confined in stalls. When they were led to the exhibition ring, they danced about, trying to show off. Each stallion seemed to say, "Just look at me."

All the horses in the exhibits were well groomed. Some had colorful ribbons braided in their manes and tails, and some wore blue ribbons, red ribbons, or white ribbons, awarded by the judges. In most cases it was clear that the judges had made good decisions.

The boys finally moved on to the other exhibits on the fairground, many of which were held in separate buildings. They looked at the exhibits of cattle, hogs, sheep, and poultry and at the exhibits of farm crops, fruits, and vegetables. Last they looked at the various exhibits of sewn and woven articles and baked and canned foods. "These exhibits of cakes and pies surely make me hungry," said Fred.

About the middle of the afternoon many of the people on the fairground crowded into the grandstand facing the large oval racetrack. They wanted to get good seats for watching the horses race at top speed around the track. The races would be the last big event of the day.

The weather was almost perfect for horse racing. The Stars and Stripes rippled in the breeze and various banners waved high above the grandstand. One banner which was stretched across the front of the grandstand read "Welcome to the St. Lawrence County Fair."

The Canton Brass Band entertained the crowd by playing several popular tunes of the day. First came the beautiful melody "Oh, Susanna," which everybody loved to hear. Next came the familiar sweet strains of "My Old Kentucky Home." The last tune was "Turkey in the Straw," with the big bass drum thumping strong accents to the delight of the crowd.

Fred and his friends separated at the grandstand, and Fred went to join his father. He and his father had made plans to watch the horse races together. Colonel Remington arrived first and hurried to pick out some seats. He called to Fred and the husky boy edged forward, pawing his way through the crowd.

"These are very good seats," said Colonel Remington. "They are near the center close to the finish line." He pointed to a rope directly in front of the judges' stand.

"Yes," said Fred. "These seats are wonderful. We can see all the way around the track and, best of all, we can see the finish line."

Already some of the trainers were on the track with their horses. They were giving the horses a few minutes' practice before the race began. The people in the grandstand watched, picking out horses that they liked or knew.

"Oh, there's George Driver in his sulky!" exclaimed Fred. "He's wearing a purple cap and driving his handsome black mare."

"Racing caps like his often are called silks," explained the Colonel, "because they usually are made of silk or silky-looking cloth. They always are bright-colored so that people can see them well to tell whose horse is ahead."

"I'm going to watch George Driver's purple silk," said Fred. "I hope his handsome black mare wins today."

The official starter waited at the starting line, and the judges and timers waited in a stand directly in front of the grandstand. The starter was the man who would shout, "Go!" at the beginning of each race. The three judges would decide which horse won first place, which second place, and which third place. The three timers, holding stop watches in their hands, would start their watches when each race began. Then they would stop the watches to tell how fast the first three horses would run.

Before long officials on horseback came out and ordered all the men and horses off the track. This was the signal that it was nearly time for the races to begin. The people in the grandstand waited calmly and quietly for the announcer to call the first race.

Almost at once five horses hitched to sulkies came out onto the track. The men driving the horses wore purple, green, red, blue, and yellow silks. "Oh, this is going to be George Driver's race," cried Fred. "I'll have to watch closely for his purple silk."

Soon the announcer in a loud voice shouted, "Ladies and Gentlemen! The first race of the afternoon will be a mile harness race of trotting horses. There are five entries. The winning prize is $100, the second prize $35, and the third prize $15."

"This will be a mile race," said Colonel Remington. "We'll have to watch closely."

"Yes," said Fred. "This track is only a half-mile long, so the horses will have to race around it twice."

Fred watched closely as the starter and his helpers worked hard to get the five horses to start from the mark at the same time. "You can

78

see that the drivers are jockeying for good positions," said the Colonel. " Each is trying to take off a little ahead of the others."

Finally after several trials, the starter shouted, "Go!" and the race began. The first time around the track the five horses kept fairly close together. As they swept by the grandstand no one could tell which horse would win. Each horse seemed to be trying hard to go faster than the other horses. "What a race!" cried Fred. "Any horse can win it."

Fred not only watched the horses but also the drivers. Most of all he watched George Driver. Loudly he cheered for Mr. Driver to win.

"The horses are still bunched," said the Colonel as they turned the last curve. "Now the judges will have to watch closely to decide which one will come in first, which second, and which third."

After the horses started down the home

stretch, George Driver's black mare pulled out ahead and crossed the finish line first. "Whee!" shouted Fred. "George Driver won!"

The people in the crowd rose to their feet and shouted and cheered. The band started to play a rollicking tune which everyone liked. Soon the excitement wore off and everyone sat down again. Fred was thrilled by the race, the cheering, and the music. Most of all, however, he was happy because his friend had won.

In a few minutes the announcer called the next race, which would be a saddle race a half mile long. This meant that men would ride horses once around the track. Soon after this race was over the announcer called the third race. All the rest of the afternoon the program of races continued. One race seemed to be just as exciting to Fred as another.

The last race of the afternoon was somewhat different from the others, because it was ex-

tremely short. "Ladies and gentlemen!" shouted the announcer in a loud voice. "Last on our program for this afternoon is a quarter horse race. This race will be a saddle race for a quarter of a mile. It will be the speediest race of the afternoon. There are six entries."

"I've never seen a quarter horse race before," said Fred.

"Well, you'll like it, because it will be extremely fast," said the Colonel. "You'll have to watch closely, though, because it won't last very long. All the horses will be little, trained for racing short distances. All the riders will wear bright-colored silks."

The Colonel pointed to the straight stretch of track in front of the grandstand. "The quarter horses will start at one end of the straightaway and dash past this grandstand like lightning. The finish line will be at the other end of the straightaway."

Immediately six restless small horses fidgeted their way to the starting line. They were so impatient that the starter and his helpers had to try several times to get them lined up for a start. "They surely seem eager to race," said Fred as he watched their lively movements.

At last the starter shouted, "Go!" and the little horses took off like a flash. They zipped past the grandstand at high speed. Only a few seconds later they crossed the finish line at the other end of the straightaway and the race was over.

The name of the winning horse was Flash. The jockey was called Tiny, because he was extremely small. He wore a bright red silk.

After the races were over, Fred and his father walked slowly along the streets homeward. Both were tired after the busy day and eager to get a good night's rest. "This has been a wonderful day," said Fred, "and just think, we'll have another wonderful day tomorrow."

Exploring the North Country

AT NINE YEARS of age Fred was exceedingly alert and active. His keen blue eyes were shaded by a shock of sandy hair, but they rarely missed anything worth seeing. He was a natural leader and bold almost to the point of daring.

St. Lawrence County was a far northern county in New York. It bordered the St. Lawrence River, which separates the United States from Canada. This country and several other northern counties formed an area known as the North Country, which was filled with woods, lakes, and streams. Fred and his friends loved the area, because it gave them an urge to explore.

84

In all seasons of the year, spring, summer, fall, and winter, they went on expeditions.

On these expeditions they often traveled far from home. They pushed long distances through the woods, roamed along Grass River, which was only a little way from home, or along Oswegatchie River, which zigzagged its way northward to the St. Lawrence River. In time they came to know much of the country well.

The boys often talked about the Algonquin and Iroquois Indians who once roamed about the North Country. These Indians had lived and hunted here before the white people came, and a few Indians still lived in parts of the area. Seldom, however, did the boys ever see any Indians on their expeditions.

There were many rumors about people who had lived in the area long before the Indians. Every now and then persons roaming the woods found remnants of crude pottery and weapons, which they believed ancient people had made. Some persons had even made excavations to gather information about these ancient people, but nothing important was ever discovered.

One bright autumn day Fred and his friends took off for a day of prowling. In spite of the bright sunshine there was a sharp nip in the air. Already Jack Frost had been out with his icy paint brush to color the leaves and loosen the nuts in the trees. Many leaves and nuts were falling to the ground.

The boys were togged out in warm clothing for their day in the woods. They wore heavy coats and caps that pulled down to protect their ears from the chilly air. They wore mittens to keep their hands warm and home-knitted stockings and sturdy boots to keep their feet warm.

In their pockets the boys carried lunches which their mothers had prepared for them to eat in the woods. These lunches consisted largely of sandwiches stuffed to overflowing with butter, ham and honey, and large ripe juicy apples for dessert.

As the boys walked along, they talked about the beautiful fall coloring. "Just look at that clump of sumac," exclaimed Fred. "See the fiery red leaves."

"Keep away from the leaves," laughed Dick. "They're too hot to touch."

"A pretty poor pun," commented Pete.

"Well, Fred called the leaves fiery red," said Dick. "He evidently meant that they are both hot and red. Maybe he can make sketches to show what he means."

"Well, if I ever do," said Fred, "I'll try to make them both fiery and red."

The boys walked on until they came to a hickory tree, from which many nuts had fallen to the ground. Suddenly Dick called out, "Freeze!" and pointed to a squirrel sitting upright under the tree. The boys froze in their tracks. They had learned this trick in order to keep from scaring small wild animals.

The squirrel held a hickory nut in its mouth which it had picked up from the ground. It had planned to hide the nut somewhere for the winter. When it had observed the boys, it had stopped. Now it must be cautious.

The boys remained frozen to see what the squirrel would do. In a few moments it dashed away with its nut to a hollow log. When it reached the open end of the log, it stopped, looked around, and hurried inside with its treasure. "That's probably its hiding place for the nut," said Fred. "Let's continue to freeze."

A moment later the squirrel came out of the hollow log without the nut. It sat upright on its haunches with its paws pressed closely against its breast. Then it cautiously crept back toward the hickory tree to pick up another nut.

Soon the squirrel became frightened and ran to the trunk of the tree. It scurried to the side opposite the boys and climbed up to the branches. Then it joined two other squirrels that were watching the boys and waiting for them to leave.

"Oh, look," said Pete. "There are two other squirrels in the tree."

"Yes, they probably dashed up there when they heard or saw us coming. Squirrels are very good climbers. They can run up trees fast."

"They also have very sharp teeth," said Dick, "almost as sharp as needles. In just a few seconds they can dig through the shell of a nut to get the meat. Usually they dig two holes in a hickory nut, but they dig four holes in walnuts or butternuts because the shells are much harder than hickory nut shells."

The boys went to peek into the end of the hollow log. "Oh, look," cried Fred. "That squirrel has stored nearly a peck of nuts inside the log. It certainly is prepared for winter. Now it can spend the coming months eating and sleeping as it chooses."

The boys wandered on through the woods. Before long they came to a chestnut tree with

90

widespreading branches. Most of the leaves and nuts had fallen from the tree. The ground beneath was almost covered with chestnuts.

"Jack Frost has been here and caused the tree to shed most of its nuts," said Fred. "I've never seen so many chestnuts in one spot."

The nuts were still covered with prickly burrs, but some of the burrs were beginning to crack open. Inside the burrs were small nuts with thin brown shells around them. "Let's get some sticks and knock off the prickly burrs," said Dick. "Then we can gather some of the nuts to take with us."

The boys found some sticks and whacked away at the nuts to loosen the burrs. "It's easy to understand why people call these nuts chestnuts," said Pete. "Each nut has a prickly little chest to protect it."

"Mother Nature does things in a wonderful way," commented Fred. "Notice that the burrs have smooth velvety linings on the inside. On the outside, however, they have sharp bristles for protection from squirrels and other animals. Right now the squirrels prefer to hunt hickory nuts and walnuts. They'll come for chestnuts after the burrs crack open."

The boys proceeded to pick up some of the fresh chestnuts. "Now we can eat our lunch and have chestnuts for dessert," said Dick. "There's a brook not far away that flows from a spring. Let's go there to get a good drink of water and to eat our lunches."

Dick led the way to the grassy bank of a sparkling little stream, where the boys sprawled out, Indian fashion, to drink the fresh water. Then they sat on the bank and ate their sandwiches and apples. Finally they finished off their lunches with some of the ripe chestnuts which they had just gathered in the woods.

By now bright sunshine flooded the woods and

banks and streams. It had transformed the chilly morning into a comfortable, pleasant afternoon. This was just the kind of afternoon that the boys liked best for exploring. With many hours still before them, they decided to saunter slowly along the banks of Grass River.

"Let's look for old pottery or weapons that might have been left along the river by the ancient people who lived here before the Indians," said Pete. "Maybe we can find some interesting pieces to take home."

The boys walked along and found a few flints which Indians had used, but they found no pottery or weapons left by the ancient people. Finally they became tired of looking and gave up the search. "Let's just look for things that are important today," said Fred.

As the boys continued walking, they saw many more squirrels hunting hickory nuts. They came across rabbits hopping here and there and nibbling at remnants of green leaves. Every now and then a rabbit hopped behind a log to hide from the boys. Then it sat upright and peeked over the log until the boys had passed.

Once as they walked along Pete called, "Freeze!" The boys stopped in their tracks and watched two groundhogs or woodchucks waddling along the bank of the river. When they saw the boys, they hustled to a hole in the bank and disappeared. "Sometime we should set some traps and catch groundhogs," Fred said. "We could sell the pelts and make some money."

Farther along the stream Dick called, "Freeze!" again. This time the boys saw a porcupine swaying along the bank. It kept on going and didn't seem to be the least bit afraid of them. "That porcupine feels safe with all its quills," said Pete with a laugh.

"I can understand why," said Fred. "I wouldn't care to come close to those quills. Let's

94

move along and leave the porcupine alone. It won't bother us if we don't bother it."

Late that afternoon the boys strolled into Canton, weary and hungry. When Fred left Pete and Dick, he said, "I surely hope Mother has a big supper tonight. I'm as hungry as a horse."

"I'm hungry, too," said Pete, "but I don't care. This has been a wonderful fall day. We won't have many more beautiful days for roaming through the woods."

Circus Days in Canton

"THIS IS THE big poster I want you to see," exclaimed Fred as he entered the *Plaindealer* office with his friends. He pointed to a large poster on the wall which told about a circus coming to town in a couple of weeks. The printing and pictures on the poster explained some of the leading attractions in the circus.

The boys crowded around the poster to learn as much as possible about the circus. A picture near the top showed a circus woman standing erect on the back of a fast-trotting horse. "Oh, see that circus performer riding that horse without holding on," said Dick.

"Yes," said Fred. "Both she and the horse are well trained. The sign says that there will be more than one hundred horses. All will be well groomed. Some will perform in the circus, others will pull the circus wagons."

"It will be a great day for you with all those horses in town," said Dick. "You'll want to bring a pencil and paper to sketch them."

"Why, of course!" replied Fred.

"Well, as for me, I want to see the wild animals in the circus," said Pete. "Just look at this picture of an elephant sitting on a box with its front feet up in the air. I hope I get to see this elephant in the circus."

The next picture showed a lion jumping through a hoop held by a lion tamer or trainer. "See this lion doing tricks," said Dick. "What would happen if the lion should get loose?"

"The lions always perform in a large iron cage," explained Fred. "The lion tamer goes into the cage with the lion, carrying a long whip. Often he cracks the whip to make the lion obey his commands."

Another picture showed a tiger peering through the bars of a cage and snarling as if eager to pounce on someone. "That tiger certainly is a wicked-looking animal," said Dick.

Still another picture attracted the boys' attention. This picture showed a circus woman riding an ostrich. "Just imagine a grown person riding a bird," said Pete.

A final picture on the poster showed some of the entertainers in the circus, including a clown making funny motions, a member of the band blowing a horn, and a juggler tossing balls into the air. "There'll be many people in the circus to help entertain us," said Fred.

The poster announced that there would be a big parade on the streets at noon and performances in both afternoon and evening.

Colonel Remington, who was busy working in his office, listened to the boys with great interest. He understood their enthusiasm, because he once had felt the same way. He remembered how excited he had been whenever a circus came to town. That was when he was still a youngster, ten or fifteen years before the War between the States.

After the boys finished looking at the poster, he showed them an article about the circus which he planned to run in the *Plaindealer*. The article told how the circus would travel to Canton during the night from another city. A man on horseback would ride ahead with a lantern to lead the way over the dusty or muddy roads.

The man on horseback would be followed by wagons loaded with the tents and other equipment. Next would come wagons with cages of wild animals in the circus. The elephants would walk. If any wagons got stuck along the way, the elephants would shove them to loosen them. All the wagons would proceed directly to the circus grounds at the edge of the town.

Soon after the circus arrived the circus people would eat breakfast and put up the big tent, or big top, and several smaller tents. They would feed and water the animals and get everything ready for the noonday parade.

The parade would start with a baton twirler, seven feet tall, marching in front of a band chariot drawn by eight white horses, hitched in four two-horse teams. There would be wagons with cages of wild animals in the circus. There would be clowns doing funny tricks and elephants trudging along. There would be a steam calliope blasting loud music.

The rest of the article told about the different acts which would take place in the afternoon and evening performances. It told how people and animals would perform in the rings in the center of the tent. All the circus people would be dressed in gay uniforms.

When the boys finished reading, Colonel Remington surprised them by saying, "How would you like to earn some tickets to the circus? I have a few tickets here which a man gave me for publishing news about the circus."

"Gee, that would be great!" exclaimed Dick. "But what can we do to earn them?"

"Help the printers clean up the print shop," said Colonel Remington.

"We'll surely try," said Pete.

Colonel Remington took the boys to the print shop. Then he told the printers that the boys would help them to wash windows and move some of the cabinets and metal type. Later he returned and gave each boy a ticket.

"Thank you!" cried Pete and Dick, proudly holding up their tickets as they started for home. "This has been a lucky day."

Fred lingered a moment longer in his father's office. "Yes, thank you," he said. "That was one of the finest things you have ever done. You made all of us very happy."

At last the day of the circus arrived. Fred's mother tapped on his door early to awaken him. He was supposed to meet Pete and Dick at the edge of the city to watch the circus arrive. No one needed to urge him to hurry. He quickly put on his clothes and dashed downstairs.

His mother already had breakfast waiting for him on the table, but he was almost too excited to eat. In a few minutes he grabbed his hat and started on his way to meet Pete and Dick. "This is going to be a grand day," he said.

Boys and girls from all over the town streamed along the streets to watch the circus arrive. The first wagons to come into sight were the tent and equipment wagons. Next came the wagons with cages of wild animals in the circus. Near the end of the caravan came the elephants, walking along at a slow pace. They flapped their big ears and held their long trunks curled up in front of them. Each seemed to know exactly where to go and what to do.

Soon after the first wagons reached the circus grounds, workmen hoisted two tents at the back of the grounds, a kitchen tent and a dining tent. Then the cooks started to prepare breakfast for the workers and performers in the circus. All were hungry because they had traveled throughout the night.

Workers placed tables and chairs in the dining tent. Soon the tables were loaded with food, including sausages and ham, fried potatoes, hot biscuits, doughnuts, and great mugs of coffee. All the circus people trooped into the tent to eat, and nobody left the table hungry.

After breakfast, all the circus workers hurried to carry out their tasks. Some of them proceeded to hoist the big top, or tent where the main performance would be held. Some laid out the rings in the center of the tent and others put up long rows of seats all around the inside. They left two spaces at the front and back of the tent for entrances.

Some workers looked after the animals in the circus. They brought special kinds of food for the animals and gave them water to drink. Most of the wild animals except the elephants were in cages. The elephants ate hay, which they picked up with their trunks to put in their mouths.

Fred and Pete and Dick watched all the preparations with great interest. "Everything runs as smoothly as clockwork," said Fred. "A couple of hours ago there was nothing here, but now a miracle city has sprung up."

"Yes, everybody seems to know just what to do and when to do it," said Pete. "Everything is put right where it belongs."

"There is no question about being ready for the parade and afternoon performance," added Dick. "I have never seen anything like it."

Shortly before noon the boys hurried downtown to find a good place to watch the parade. Now that they had seen the circus arrive, they were especially eager to see it parade. Crowds filled the sidewalks and some watched from second-story windows along the way.

First in the parade came a tall, slender baton twirler, spinning and flashing his baton. Next came a great band chariot, drawn by eight white horses, hitched in four teams of two horses each. The members of the band wore bright red uniforms with gold braid trimmings and very high shakos or plumes. They played constantly and their blaring music echoed up and down the street of the town.

Fred watched and listened closely but gave most attention to the eight white horses drawing

the chariot. He marveled at the skill of the driver, who sat on a seat at the front of the chariot. He could see that all the horses were exceedingly well trained.

Near the middle of the parade came freakish-looking clowns, doing funny tricks. Later came three plodding elephants, walking after one another. The second elephant grasped the tail of the first elephant with its trunk, and the third elephant grasped the tail of the second elephant with its trunk. Atop the first elephant rode a man dressed in an elaborate oriental costume. At the very end of the parade came the calliope blasting loud music.

As soon as the parade ended, the boys hurried back to the circus grounds. They walked past the animal cages containing lions, tigers, monkeys, and many other interesting creatures. They stopped to watch the elephants, standing quietly side by side. Each elephant was secured by a heavy chain around one leg to keep it from wandering away.

During the afternoon performance, Fred gave particular attention to the horses. He observed how intelligent they were and how well they understood the signs and commands. He noted how gracefully and quickly they moved from place to place. Every now and then he took out a pencil and paper to sketch one of them.

At the close of the performance, Fred said good-by to his friends and walked slowly home. He was completely exhausted but happy over the many exciting things he had seen during the day. "Nobody will have to rock me to sleep tonight," he said as he entered the house.

Mrs. Remington smiled as he dropped into a comfortable chair and readily understood how he felt. "Yes, you have had a long busy day," she said. "Sit down and eat supper. Then go right up to bed and get a good night's rest."

Fred was even too tired to talk. He went upstairs to his room, undressed, and fell into bed. Within a short time he was fast asleep, dreaming of prancing horses, lumbering elephants, roaring lions and tigers, daring acrobats, funny clowns, a brass band, and a blaring steam calliope.

The next morning Fred could hardly believe that the circus had left. "I surely wish everyday was circus day," he said.

Growing Interest in Horses

"YEP, THERE ARE horses all over the western plains," said a stranger as Fred entered the *Plaindealer* office one day. Fred overheard this remark and paused to look at the stranger. He noticed that the stranger was dressed like a man from the western frontier.

"Mr. Beard, I want you to meet my son, Frederic," said Colonel Remington.

The stranger extended his hand. "Howdy, Frederic," he said. "I'm Samuel Beard and I'm glad to meet you. Your father has just told me that you are greatly interested in horses."

"Yes, sir, Mr. Beard," said Fred enthusiasti-

110

cally. "Horses are my favorite animals. I like to watch them and I like to draw them, too."

"Well, in that case you should go to the plains country," said Mr. Beard. "There you would find thousands and thousands of horses, mostly broncos. Also you would find many cowboys, trappers, Indians, and soldiers, but the horses far outnumber the people."

Mr. Beard looked the part of a man from the frontier. He was tall and slender and his skin was weathered and tanned. He had a sweeping mustache and coal black hair that reached to his shoulders. He wore a leather jacket and high leather boots.

Meeting Mr. Beard was only one of many experiences that helped to arouse Fred's interest in the western frontier. Every now and then persons stopped in Canton who were planning to take long trips to the West. Some planned to move to the West with their families and all their belongings. Most persons from the East now traveled westward by railroad, but formerly they had traveled in big covered wagons pulled by horses or oxen.

Other persons stopped in Canton who had already been in the West. These persons told exciting stories about cowboys and Indians, both of whom were very skillful horsemen. The cowboys used horses to watch over herds of cattle in the great open country. The Indians used horses to go hunting and to migrate to new homes.

All these experiences seemed to strengthen Fred's interest in horses. From the time he had lived with his grandparents beside the county fairground, he had seen horses and had come to know horses. He had seen horses working on farms and pulling loads on city streets. He had seen horses being driven hitched to carriages or being ridden to transport people. Horses were very important in everyday living.

Fred had reached many important conclusions about horses. Horses were different, just as people were different. Some were good for one purpose, and some for another. Horses were very intelligent and friendly. Some became family pets and others could be trained to entertain people by racing or doing tricks.

Horses obeyed orders. Cowboys' horses learned to come when the cowboys whistled. Circus horses learned to keep time to music and to bow to audiences. Horses hitched to milk wagons learned to stand still on streets while the drivers carried milk into houses.

Horses had good memories. They readily learned to follow spoken directions, telling them to start, stop, turn right, or turn left. They even learned to interpret the tone of their masters' voices, which indicated whether their masters were in good humor or bad humor.

Horses had very good vision and could see exceedingly well at night. Furthermore, they could move one eye to look forward and the other eye to look backward. Thus they could keep moving forward and at the same time observe what, if anything, was following them.

Horses had a very good sense of smell. They knew the odors of their masters and were skeptical of the odors of strangers. They would snort disapproval if they smelled the odor of something they disliked to eat or an unwanted animal in their stalls.

Through the years Fred had drawn many sketches of horses, but he was never satisfied with his sketches. Always he wondered how he could show that horses were intelligent and friendly. How could he show that horses had good memories and obeyed well? How could he show that horses could see and smell well? He must keep on practicing until his sketches would show horses as they really were in everyday life.

The Remington family often talked about horses at mealtime, because both Colonel Remington and Fred were interested. One evening when Fred came into the house, he asked, "Mother, what are we having for supper?"

"We're going to have venison steak, baked potatoes, hot rolls, and honey," she replied. Then she added with a wry smile, "These probably will be served with horse-talk sauce."

Fred laughed at his mother's remark and said, "I'll leave it to Father to furnish the horse-talk sauce, but he'll be ready."

Soon Colonel Remington came striding into the house to join his wife and son. Almost immediately after the family sat down to eat, he said, "I just had a good talk with my friend, Walter Van Valkenburg, whose horse Nellie won one of the races at the county fair."

Fred and his mother gave each other a knowing look. Fred listened in rapt attention as his father described Van Valkenburg as an excellent trainer. "I think he is an exceptional man at handling horses," said the Colonel.

"I agree," said Fred. "I've watched him work with horses and I watched him with you when he

116

won that race. Nellie was a very good horse, but he was also a topnotch driver."

"Yes," said the Colonel earnestly. "Van Valkenburg's skill in handling horses comes from knowing and treating horses well. He respects horses and they respect him. Nellie won that race largely because he was driving her. He understood her and she understood him."

The talk went on and on. Finally Colonel Remington said, "You're interested in horses, Fred, and I'm interested in horses. Someday I should like to go into the business of owning and racing horses. Then I would employ Van Valkenburg as my manager and trainer."

"Oh, gee!" exclaimed Fred. "That would be a wonderful thing to do."

Bee Hunting

ONE EARLY FALL evening Fred came bouncing into the living room greatly excited. "Father," he exclaimed, "What is bee hunting? I just heard some men here in town talking about going bee hunting. I know about hunting such animals as rabbits, squirrels, ducks, and geese, but I never heard about hunting bees. Why does anyone want to hunt bees?"

Colonel Remington was highly amused by Fred's curiosity. "Well, my son," he explained, "people hunt bees for their honey. They have to find the bees in order to get the honey. Hunting bees for honey has gone on for hundreds and

118

hundreds of years. Honey is mentioned many times in the Bible, even in Genesis, the very first book of the Bible.

"Bees once played an important part in fighting wars. Ancient cities were protected by great walls, with soldiers watching inside. If enemy soldiers came to attack, the defenders often tossed beehives over the walls. Quickly the bees flew out of the hives and started to sting the attacking soldiers. Then the soldiers ran fast to escape because the bees stung them with devastating effect.

"Many people here in Canton and in the country round about keep hives of bees. Each fall they take out some of the honey and leave the rest for the bees to eat. Other bees live in the woods and make their homes and store their honey in hollow trees. When people go bee hunting, they try to find where the bees live in hollow trees in order to get the honey."

Fred listened closely as his father talked about bees and their honey. "Of course I know that bees make honey, but I never knew that people hunt bees to get honey," he said. "Sometime when I go to the woods I might like to try hunting bees, but I wouldn't know what to do."

"I have a good friend, Dave Hartwell, who is a bee hunter," said Colonel Remington. "Possibly he would be willing to take you along on one of his hunting trips."

"Oh, I hope he will," said Fred.

A few days later when Fred entered the *Plaindealer* office, he found Dave Hartwell talking with his father. "Well, you came just in time," Colonel Remington said. "Mr. Hartwell, this is my son Frederic."

Mr. Hartwell shook hands with Fred. "I'm certainly glad to know you," he said with a friendly smile. "Your father has just told me that you are interested in bee hunting."

"Yes, but all that I know about bee hunting is what Father has told me," said Fred. "I never even knew that people go bee hunting until I overheard some men talking about it one day on the street."

"Well, they certainly do, and I'll be glad to show you what it is like," said Mr. Hartwell. "Next Tuesday a friend of mine, Bud Wright, and I plan to go bee hunting, provided it's a good sunshiny day. If you should like to go with us, come to my house before eight o'clock in the morning. Then, if the weather is right, the three of us will take off for the woods."

Fred's face took on a broad grin. "I'll be there before eight o'clock, all ready to go," he said. "Then, if you'll tell me what to do, I'll help you all I can."

On Tuesday morning Fred arrived early at Mr. Hartwell's home, ahead of Bud Wright. Mr. Hartwell brought out a small wooden box about the size of a cigar box. "While we're waiting," he said, "I'll show you this bee box, which we use to help us locate a bee tree, or a tree where bees have stored honey.

"Notice that the box is divided into two sections, a top section and a bottom section," he continued. "The top section has a sliding glass cover and there is a sliding metal partition between the top section and the bottom section. The bottom section contains a piece of honeycomb covered with sugar syrup."

Mr. Hartwell handed the box to Fred so that he could see how it worked. Fred slid both the glass cover and the metal partition back and forth. He noticed the piece of honeycomb in the bottom section covered with sugar syrup. "I still don't understand how you use the box to help you find a bee tree," he said.

"Well, I'll explain," said Mr. Hartwell. "All the bees that gather nectar are females, called workers. When we reach the woods, I'll look for a worker collecting nectar from a flower and I'll stalk her with the box just as a hunter stalks a deer or a squirrel with a gun. First I'll open the glass cover and slip the box directly under the bee. Then suddenly I'll close the glass cover and trap her in the top section of the box so that she can't get away.

"The bee will struggle to escape, bumping herself against the glass cover, but I'll open the metal partition to let her come into contact with the honeycomb covered with sugar syrup. Almost at once she will stick out her mop-like tongue to suck up the sweet syrup. Within about thirty seconds she will completely fill the honey sac in her body.

"When she is ready to leave with her sac of honey, I'll open the glass top so she can fly home. For a moment she will hover about the box, but soon she'll start to fly in circles, ever wider and higher until she is about thirty feet above the ground. Then suddenly she will start to fly home in a straight line, which we often call a beeline."

"The bee must have very good eyes in order to find her way home," said Fred.

"Yes, she has two large compound eyes, one on each side of her head," explained Mr. Hartwell. "Each of her compound eyes is made up of many small eyes close together. In addition, she has three small eyes in the center of her head. With all these eyes there is very little danger of her getting lost."

Next Mr. Hartwell showed Fred another interesting device called a smoker. "Notice that this smoker has bellows which we can work to make it throw out clouds of smoke," he said. "We use the smoker to make the bees groggy so they won't sting us while we take the honey from the hollow tree."

At this stage in the conversation, Bud Wright

arrived. Immediately Mr. Hartwell stopped talking and pointed out what each person should carry to the woods. He himself would carry the bee box, the smoker, some veils to protect their heads and gloves to protect their hands. Mr. Wright was to carry an ax, a hatchet, and a big crosscut saw. Fred was to carry two large buckets or pails, one inside the other.

After the three bee hunters reached the woods, Mr. Hartwell led the way to an open place where goldenrod plants were blooming. The humming of bees could be heard as they settled on the flowers to gather nectar and then took off for their homes. "This is a good place to start," said Mr. Hartwell, sniffing the air.

He spotted a bee on a flower and quietly moved toward her with his bee box. He held the box just below her with the glass cover open. Then suddenly he closed the glass cover and trapped her in the top section of the box.

At first the bee fluttered in the box, trying to escape. Then Mr. Hartwell opened the metal partition and she pounced on the honeycomb covered with sugar syrup in the lower section. At once she was content and started to fill her sac with the sweet liquid. Within about thirty seconds she was ready to take off. "Now watch her," said Mr. Hartwell.

The bee flew out of the box and started to fly in small circles. Round and round she flew in ever larger and higher circles. When she was about thirty feet high, she suddenly flew off in a straight line toward her home.

Mr. Hartwell pointed to help Fred follow the bee as she flew away. "She'll fly to her home in a hollow tree, empty her honey sac, and report to her fellow workers. Then in from ten to twenty minutes she'll come back with several other workers. In the meantime, I must open the bee box to be ready for them."

He looked at his watch and placed the bee box in the same position as before. Within fifteen minutes the busy bee returned with several other workers. She was cautious about entering the box, but soon she and the other bees settled on the honeycomb and began to pack their honey sacs. About thirty seconds later, they flew about in spirals and took off in a beeline for home in a hollow tree. Mr. Hartwell, Mr. Wright, and Fred watched closely to determine in which directions the bees flew.

"Now let's try to find the hollow tree where the bees are storing their honey," said Mr. Hartwell. "We must be careful to keep going in the right direction."

The bee hunters struggled through the dense underbrush of the forest. They passed several dead trees along the way, but Mr. Hartwell merely looked up at them and shook his head. Finally they came to a dead oak tree that attracted his attention. He tapped the tree and found that it was hollow. He placed his ear against the tree and listened. Then he looked up and caught a glimpse of bees entering and leaving through a knothole about fifty feet high. "This is the tree we're looking for," he said.

He explained that it would be necessary to fell the tree in order to get the honey. At once he and Mr. Wright began to cut across the trunk of the tree with the crosscut saw and the ax. "Fred, get the smoker ready," he called.

The smoker, which Mr. Wright had already shown Fred before leaving home, was a metal can stuffed with slow-burning rags and burlap. On one side it had a spout and on the other side small bellows which could be worked to force smoke out through the spout.

Soon the big oak tree fell with a mighty crash. Immediately the bee hunters put gloves on their hands and draped veils over their heads. They rushed toward the knothole where the bees came swarming forth. Fred pumped the bellows of the smoker and puffs of smoke filled the air. The smoke made the bees groggy.

129

Mr. Hartwell chopped a large hole in the tree near the knothole and found the cavity filled with honey. Then he and Mr. Wright scooped up the honeycomb and filled the two large buckets which Fred had carried to the woods. "There still is some honeycomb left," he said, "but soon bears, raccoons, or skunks will come to clear out the rest of it."

The bee hunters now gathered up their equipment and started home with the two buckets of honeycomb. "We're glad you could come with us, Fred," said Mr. Hartwell. "You have been a good sport and a big help."

"Thank you," said Fred. "I certainly appreciate your allowing me to come with you. Now I understand what bee hunting is like."

All on a Spring Day

ONE FRIDAY afternoon in April the weather was unusually warm. The air in the schoolroom was stuffy and the children were eager for the day to end. As Fred and his friends, Pete and Dick, left the building, Pete said, "I feel an attack of spring fever coming on."

"So do I," said Fred. "Let's plan to spend tomorrow in the woods. Then we can get the spring fever out of our systems."

On the way home the boys heard a peculiar honking sound high above them. They looked up and spotted a flock of wild geese, flying northward in a great wedge formation. "Oh, look at those wild geese!" cried Dick. "They're on their way to Canada to spend the summer."

"Their flying to Canada means that spring is on the way," said Fred. "I marvel at how they can tell just when to fly northward for the summer. Soon they will build nests, lay eggs, and raise many young geese. Then in October or November all of them will fly back to spend the winter in the southland."

The next morning the boys, wearing sweaters and caps, took off for the woods. The sky was clear and bright sunshine sifted down through the leafless trees. "Whew!" exclaimed Fred. "This is going to be a warm day. Let's peel off our sweaters."

As the boys continued to ramble, they looked about for signs of spring. Soon Pete spotted a spring flower. "Oh, look!" he cried excitedly. "Here's a Johnny-jump-up."

The other boys stooped down to look closely

at the small violet which was just beginning to show its delicate colors. "Now we know that spring is really here, with geese flying northward, violets blooming, and boys peeling off their sweaters," said Fred.

The boys pushed on through the woods. Suddenly they came upon a groundhog, or woodchuck, sauntering along in the underbrush. "That groundhog is out stuffing himself after his long sleep," said Pete. "Groundhog day is February 2nd. There is an old saying that if a groundhog sees his shadow on February 2nd, he goes back to sleep for another six weeks."

"This is April, so he should be wide awake by now," said Fred. "He has to store up a lot of fat through the warm months to keep him alive during his long winter sleep."

By now the boys were tired and hungry. They sat down on a log to eat hearty lunches of sandwiches, cookies, and apples, which their mothers

had prepared. After they finished eating, they headed for one of their favorite trails along Grass River, a short distance away.

When the boys reached the banks of Grass River, they found many frogs hopping into the water. These frogs had spent the winter in holes in the banks, but now they were out hopping about. One large frog jumped off a bank directly in front of Pete. "Wham!" cried Pete. "That big frog surely jumped in a hurry. Let's look in the water to see whether we can find any frog's eggs or tadpoles."

"Yes, here are some eggs," said Fred. "Look at this mass of jelly. It probably contains hundreds of eggs."

Almost immediately Dick discovered some tadpoles wiggling their way through the cloudy water. He reached into the water and brought up one of them to examine. "It still has a long tail, but its hind legs are beginning to grow," he said. "Once it's able to use its hind legs well, it will lose its tail."

By now the boys were growing quite warm from walking in the hot sun. "Let's take off our shoes and stockings," said Dick, "and give our feet and legs a little airing."

The boys sat on the bank and stuck their feet cautiously into the water. The cold water felt good as they moved their feet about and wriggled their toes. Suddenly Pete turned to Fred and said, "I dare you to peel off your clothes and take a dip in the river."

"I never take a dare," answered Fred as he began to undress.

"Nor I either," exclaimed Pete, starting to pull off his clothes.

The two boys stood briefly side by side on the bank. They realized that it was early in the year and that the water would be extremely cold. "Let's jump in together," said Pete.

Both boys hesitated for a moment, but finally jumped into the stream together. "Wowie!" cried Pete, immediately starting to scramble toward the bank. "This water is full of icicles!"

"Yes, I'm frozen already," said Fred, hurrying to the bank. "I knew the water would be cold, but I just couldn't take a dare. It will take many days of sunshine to make that water warm enough for swimming."

Dick quickly started a fire on the bank and Fred and Pete sat down beside it to dry themselves. "My, that fire feels good," said Pete with his teeth chattering. "I want to get back into my clothes as fast as I can."

"So do I," said Fred, starting to dress. "I've had enough of early spring swimming."

Ordinarily both Fred and Pete loved to swim and did much swimming during the summer. Fred had a good reputation as a swimmer and was considered one of the best swimmers for his

137

age around Canton. Never before, however, had he tried to swim in cold icy water.

After Fred and Pete got dressed, Dick teased them about scrambling out so fast. "I thought you were braver than that," he said.

"You just don't know how cold that water really is," said Pete.

That afternoon after the boys returned to Canton, Fred decided to walk past the fairground on the way home. He walked through the gate and went to the stables where the horses were kept. Soon he found George Driver grooming a three-year-old mare in one of the stalls.

"I'm glad to see you," said Mr. Driver. "I've missed you through the cold winter months and was hoping you would come by. This warm spring day is just right to bring out a horseman."

Fred was greatly pleased to be called a horseman, but already Mr. Driver knew that Fred liked horses and that he was a good judge of horses. He still was only a growing boy, but he knew more about horses than many adults.

"I'm almost ready to take this mare, Betsy, out on the track for a light workout," Mr. Driver continued. "I want to note her natural trotting stride and will not urge her to speed. If you have time to stay and watch, I'll appreciate your telling me what you think of her."

"Oh, I have time," said Fred. "I'll be glad to watch her."

Soon Mr. Driver hitched Betsy to a sulky. He checked her harness carefully to make certain that every buckle and strap was fastened. Then he mounted the sulky and started to drive her around the track. Fred watched her very carefully and noted that she had a beautiful rhythmic stride. "That Betsy is an exceptional horse," he said to himself. "With a little practice she'll make a wonderful race horse."

At the end of the exercise Mr. Driver stopped

near the stable. "Well, Fred," he said, "what do you think of her?"

"Oh, I like her!" exclaimed Fred. "She seems to be almost perfect and will make a great race horse someday. I've never seen a horse with a better stride."

"Thank you," said Mr. Driver. "I'm glad you like her and I appreciate your watching, because you are a good judge of horses."

Fred felt grateful to Mr. Driver for being called a good judge of horses. "I'll be back to see you soon," he said as he turned to leave. "I must go home for supper now."

When Fred reached home, his father had already come from the *Plaindealer* office. "Well, Fred, what have you done today?" he asked.

"The most exciting thing I've done was to help George Driver judge a three-year-old mare at the racetrack," replied Fred. Then he told the full story of what had happened.

Changes in t Making

ONE EVENING Fred stood at the window, watching for Colonel Remington to come home for dinner. Soon he spotted his father coming but walking much faster than usual. He wondered why his father seemed to be in such a hurry.

Colonel Remington strode into the living room, brushed past Fred, and called to his wife, "Clara, I have a big surprise for you. I have just been appointed U. S. Collector of the Port of Ogdensburg on the St. Lawrence River. Here is a telegram announcing my appointment."

Mrs. Remington took the telegram and read it several times. "What does receiving this appointment mean?" she asked. "Does it mean that we'll have to sell our house here in Canton and move to Ogdensburg?"

All the while Fred had been listening, wondering what was going to happen. "Yes, will we have to move to Ogdensburg?" he asked.

"Not at once," replied Colonel Remington. "For a while I'll continue to edit the *Plaindealer* and travel back and forth between Canton and Ogdensburg. Then I'll try to get someone to look after the business of printing and mailing the paper."

"I hope you keep on including stories about horses and horse racing," exclaimed Fred.

The Colonel smiled. "Don't worry," he said. "As long as I have anything to do with the *Plaindealer*, I'll include stories about horses and horse racing."

Colonel Remington always had been interested in horses. His experiences as a cavalry officer greatly strengthened his interest. Now in nearly every issue of the *Plaindealer* he managed to carry an article or two about horses.

Almost immediately Colonel Remington took over his position as Collector of the Port of Ogdensburg. He continued to edit the *Plaindealer* and proceeded to travel back and forth between Canton and Ogdensburg. In the meantime he arranged for his brother, Lamartine Remington, to manage the *Plaindealer*.

For a couple of years Colonel Remington divided his time between Canton and Ogdensburg. All the while Fred was content to keep on living in Canton. He had spent all his life here and looked upon it as home. He knew all the streets and buildings in the town and all the woods and streams in the surrounding country.

During these years, as Fred continued to grow, he became more and more interested in sports and outdoor activities. He swam almost daily during the summer and was proud of his record of being the best swimmer for his age in Canton. He was a good fisherman and knew the best places to fish in all the streams and lakes. He also was a good boatman and could manage a canoe with great skill.

At the same time Fred kept up his interest in horses. He read all the articles about horses which his father published in the *Plaindealer*. He continued to observe horses closely on the racetrack and came to know the names of many horses and drivers.

One day when Colonel Remington came home from the *Plaindealer* office, he said, "Fred, I have good news for you. I wonder whether you can guess what the good news is."

"Are you going to give up your position in Ogdensburg and stay in Canton all the time?" asked Fred. "That would be good news."

"No," laughed Colonel Remington. "Do you

remember that I once said I might go into the horse business with Walter Van Valkenburg? Well, Van and I have formed a partnership to keep a few race horses. He will care for the horses, train them, and drive them in races."

"Oh, gee!" cried Fred. "That's the best news I've heard in a long time. Maybe Van will let me help him work with the horses."

Soon Fred and Van became very close friends and Fred visited the stables nearly every day. As Fred had hoped, Van let him help to feed, groom, and exercise some of the horses. Fred was large for his age and could handle the horses almost as well as Van. Gradually he came to know the horses well and they came to know him. The horses liked him and seemed eager to obey his commands.

All the while Fred kept up his interest in drawing. Every few days he made sketches of some of the horses, especially when the horses were

exercising. Also he made sketches when he was engaging in outdoor activities with his friends, including such activities as swimming, fishing, and boating.

Gradually Fred became widely acquainted around Canton. One of his good friends was J. Henry Rushton, who built canoes for people to use on nearby streams and lakes. He built the canoes in his barn, which was located fairly close to the street.

One day when Fred and Pete walked past the barn, they noticed that Mr. Rushton was working on the inside. "Let's stop to see him," said Pete. "He's building another canoe."

"Yes, he's an expert in building canoes," said Fred. "His canoes are well-shaped and beautiful to watch floating on the water. When he finishes a canoe it is almost perfect."

The boys walked toward the barn and stood for a moment in the open doorway. "Come in, fellows," said Mr. Rushton, looking up from his work. "I've just put the final touches on this cedar canoe. Look it over carefully and tell me how you like it."

"It looks wonderful to me," exclaimed Fred. "You have done an excellent job."

"Well," said Mr. Rushton, "I always try to do my best, but I guess I'm never satisfied."

"You certainly should be," said Pete. "This is a beautiful canoe."

"I've tried to give it a very smooth surface," said Mr. Rushton, proudly running his hand over the outside of the canoe. "It's almost as smooth as silk, and the cedar wood smells as fragrant as a rose."

Mr. Rushton invited the boys to sit in the canoe. They climbed in and could almost feel themselves floating along on the water of a stream or lake. "Wouldn't it be wonderful to own a canoe like this?" said Pete.

After the boys climbed out, Fred said, "Now, Mr. Rushton, will you let me make a sketch of you sitting in the canoe? I would like to make a sketch to add to my collection."

Mr. Rushton began to chuckle. "Of course you may make a sketch of me sitting in the canoe. I understand that you draw pictures well, especially pictures of horses."

Fred was greatly pleased by this remark. He drew a quick sketch of Mr. Rushton sitting in the canoe. Afterward Mr. Rushton held the sketch in his hand to examine it. "Why, it's really good," he said with a smile.

Little did Fred realize that in the years ahead J. Henry Rushton would become widely known for his skill in making canoes. Nor did he realize that he would use one of Mr. Rushton's canoes in exploring rivers and lakes.

One morning late in August, 1873, Fred came down to breakfast hungry as usual. Within a few minutes he consumed three fried eggs and six strips of bacon. Then he turned to a stack of griddle cakes which he topped with golden butter and maple syrup.

Fred's mother was happy to see her son eat so heartily. "I'm pleased to see you enjoy your breakfast," she said.

"Yes," said Fred, "I'm glad I have a mother who is such a good cook. Your cooking certainly hasn't stunted my growth."

At this remark both Fred and his mother began to laugh. Soon Fred would be twelve years old, but he looked as if he might be going on fifteen. Good food and outdoor activities were combining to make him a robust young man.

That afternoon Fred and his friends Pete and Dick planned to go fishing. About the middle of the forenoon he went out on the porch to check his fishing tackle. Within a few minutes he noted his father coming down the street. "Mother," he called, "Father is coming home. Why is he coming home at this time of day?"

Mrs. Remington was surprised, too, and came to the porch. The Colonel strode directly to the porch and started to talk. "I have important news for you," he said abruptly. "I have just sold the *Plaindealer.* Now within a few weeks we'll move to Ogdensburg."

Fred dropped his fishing tackle on the porch to listen. He had known for some time that his father planned to sell the *Plaindealer,* but somehow he had never taken the matter seriously. Now the paper had been sold and the family would move to Ogdensburg. "How soon will you let the people know?" asked Mrs. Remington.

"I have just written an announcement to publish in the next issue of the paper," said Colonel Remington.

"What will you do about Walter Van Valkenburg and our horses?" asked Fred.

"Van Valkenburg will move to Ogdensburg with our horses," replied the Colonel. "Then we'll probably purchase a few more horses after we get located there."

"Golly!" exclaimed Fred. "We're going to move and Van is going to move with the horses. What a story to tell my pals!"

A couple of hours later Fred hurried off to meet his friends. He could hardly wait to tell them the news. "Hey, fellows," he called as he came near, "I have big news for you."

"What big news?" asked Pete.

"Well, you'll be surprised," said Fred. "My father has sold the *Plaindealer* and we're going to move to Ogdensburg in a few weeks. That's the big news in a nutshell."

"What are you going to do about the horses?" asked Dick.

"Oh, Walter Van Valkenburg will move to Ogdensburg, too, with our horses," replied Fred.

152

"Then we may even buy more horses after we get located there."

"We're certainly going to miss you, Fred," said Pete. "Life won't be the same around here after you leave."

"And I'm going to miss you," said Fred, "but Ogdensburg isn't far away. You could come there to see me and I'll come back to see you."

During the next couple of weeks, the Remingtons were busy packing. Soon the whole house was filled with boxes, tubs, and barrels. Some were filled to overflowing with small objects. Others were only partly filled.

Bedsteads were taken down and the quilts and blankets were used for wrapping articles to keep them from breaking. Pieces of china and glassware and other breakable items were carefully wrapped before they were packed. The large grandfather clock, which had stood in a hall, looked like a baby bundled in a thick comforter.

153

Fred thought that it looked a little like an ancient Egyptian mummy.

On moving day all the Remington belongings were loaded into wagons. Colonel and Mrs. Remington rode on one of the wagons. All the wagons were pulled by heavy work horses.

Walter Van Valkenburg took charge of moving the horses to Ogdensburg. Some of the horses were ridden, and some were led. Much to Fred's delight, he was permitted to travel with Van and the horses.

Almost immediately after the Remingtons settled in Ogdensburg, the boys of the city accepted Fred as a leader. They called him "Puffy" because of his plumpness and admired him for his prowess in swimming, fishing, and canoeing. Many looked upon him as a hero because of his ability in outdoor sports.

Fred always managed to spend many happy hours with Van and the horses, often to make sketches of the horses. He knew each horse in the stables and noted its differences from all the others. He knew its name, nature, and temperament as well as its record.

At school in Ogdensburg, Fred manifested great interest in drawing. His urge to become an artist became stronger and stronger and he scarcely could be found without a pencil and drawing pad in hand. Often his urge to draw caused him to neglect studying his books.

New People and Places

WHEN FRED was fourteen years of age, his parents decided that he was old enough to send away to school. They were eager for him to have a good education and arranged to send him to a small church school for boys, which had been established only a few years before. This new school was the Vermont Episcopal Institute at Burlington, Vermont.

Fred soon made new friends among the boys at the Institute. He enjoyed hiking with them through the hills and mountains of Vermont and along the shores of Lake Champlain, a few miles away. All the while he continued to draw.

156

In the summer of 1876, Colonel Remington, influenced by his military background, decided to transfer Fred from the church school to a military school. He was proud of his own military background and wanted his son to have some of the advantages of military training. Finally he arranged for Fred to enroll at Highland Military Academy, Worcester, Massachusetts.

That year stories of a great disaster had come from the West. General George A. Custer, a hero in the War between the States, had led a cavalry attack against the Indians under Chief Sitting Bull. The battle had been fought near the Little Big Horn River in Montana. Custer and all his men had been killed.

News of this disastrous defeat by the Indians spread slowly through the East. The cadets at Highland Military Academy became greatly excited. All of them were interested in the West as a land of cowboys, Indians, and soldiers, with horses as the chief means of transportation. They wondered what Custer's defeat might mean.

By now Fred was five feet eight inches tall and tipped the scales at 180 pounds. He made a pleasing, robust appearance in his new military uniform. Almost as soon as he enrolled he became known as "Bud" Remington.

Fred liked the rugged life at the Academy but disliked the monotonous routine and the strict discipline. He engaged in the school athletics and sports with enthusiasm, but wanted to feel free to take off on occasional exploratory trips through the surrounding country. He missed all the freedom that he had enjoyed before.

As usual, he quickly made friends at the Academy. One of his closest friends was Julian Wilder, a classmate who also liked to draw. The two cadets spent much of their time together and often showed their sketches to each other. One day Julian received a letter from a friend of his named Scott Turner, who lived in Augusta, Maine. "Just look at this letter from an artist friend of mine," said Julian. "He has covered the margins with sketches."

Fred was pleasantly surprised as he glanced at the sketches on the letter. "Say, that fellow is really good," he said. "Who is he?"

"He's a young man who has been studying art in Augusta," said Julian. "He is almost as crazy about sketching as you are."

"Would you mind if I write him a letter about his sketches?" asked Fred.

"Of course not," replied Julian. "He'll be pleased to hear from you."

Fred wrote a long letter to Scott Turner, telling how much he liked his drawings. He told Turner that he liked to draw but that he did not pretend to draw well. He asked Turner to send him a sheet of sketches. Then he would use the sketches for guidance.

Fred and Turner exchanged letters through-out the two years that Fred attended Highland Military Academy. In one of his letters Fred enclosed his picture with the comment, "You can burn it up, but don't throw it into the back yard or it may scare some wandering hen to death."

In another letter to Turner Fred covered the top of the sheet with sketches. Then beneath he wrote, "I hope you will excuse these blots I got on the upper end of this paper."

In still another letter to Turner, he asked for a group sketch and said, "Please send me a drawing of a battle between Russians and Turks or between Indians and soldiers."

At this stage in his artwork Fred was beginning to paint as well as to draw. During the summer after his first year at the Academy, he completed his first full-scale oil painting. This painting, which he called "The Captive Gaul," showed a Gallic chief securely chained in a

Roman prison. Standing back of the chief was a Roman guard closely watching him.

Fred found painting very exciting and set up a temporary studio during his vacation. Then he painted many horses that belonged to people in the neighborhood. Often he asked people to lend him their horses to paint.

By the summer of 1878, Colonel Remington realized that Fred was not suited to a military career and began to look for a place to send him to art school. In his search he discovered that Yale University at New Haven, Connecticut, planned to start a new art department and would accept students for the following year. At once he decided that this new school would be a good place for Fred.

That evening while he and the other members of the family were eating supper, he suddenly looked over at his son and said, "Fred, it's evident that you aren't interested in a military

career. How would you like to study art at Yale University this coming year?"

"I would like it very much provided the university doesn't try to make a sissy out of me," replied Fred.

Both Colonel and Mrs. Remington could see little danger of their rugged, oversized son becoming a sissy. "There is little chance of that ever happening," said the Colonel. "What do you think of the idea?"

"Well, I like the idea," replied Fred. "For one thing, Yale has a great football team. There is nothing very sissy about football."

That fall Fred took off to enter the new art department of Yale University. The courses in the new department were based chiefly on European artists and techniques, which Fred found very boring. There were only two students in the department, Poultney Bigelow and Frederic Remington, both about the same age.

Bigelow had attended school in Europe, where his father had been a distinguished diplomat. He was interested chiefly in literature and hoped someday to become a writer. He had no interest whatever in football, which he considered a messy kind of game.

Fred, on the other hand, had very little interest in literature and writing. He had grown up roaming through the woods of the North Country in New York. He liked rugged activities and he thoroughly enjoyed engaging in scrimmages on the football field.

These two young men, so different in tastes, became great friends. Bigelow was on his way to becoming a famous writer and Remington to becoming a distinguished artist. They quickly called each other Big and Fred.

Bigelow was editor of the *Current,* a weekly student publication at the University. He invited Fred to illustrate the publication, and Fred dotted its pages with cartoons. The students were delighted with these humorous cartoons, but the professor of the art department was shocked. He felt that drawing cartoons was disgraceful to his department.

Nearly every day after school opened, Fred went to the nearby athletic field to watch the boys practice football. He was eager to join the boys on the field, but didn't know how to proceed. "How can I become a player?" he asked a member of the squad.

"Get a player's suit in the dressing room and report to the coach," replied the player. "I'm sure he will let you play."

Fred streaked to the dressing room and a few minutes later was on the field ready to learn the game. The coach readily accepted him because he had the size, weight, and muscle needed for football. With a little practice he should make a strong member of the team.

The captain of the team was Walter Camp, who later became a noted authority on football. He and Fred became close friends and two of the best members of the team. They helped the team to win several important games during the season. The climax came at the end of the season when the two of them helped defeat Princeton University, one of Yale's strongest rivals. Now they were regarded as heroes.

Fred played football for two seasons at Yale University. In 1879, following the end of the football season, he looked forward to going home for Christmas vacation. He wouldn't admit to being homesick, but he actually was eager to return to Ogdensburg for a couple of weeks. He was eager to see his parents, and he also was eager to see Walter Van Valkenburg and the horses.

When Fred arrived at Ogdensburg by train, he was surprised to find only his mother waiting at

166

the station to greet him. "Where is Father?" he asked anxiously.

"Your father is ill and couldn't come out in this cold weather," replied his mother. "He is waiting at home to greet you and hear about your experiences at Yale. Van will drive us there in the carriage."

Van shook hands with Fred when he reached the carriage and said, "We've been hearing great things about you playing football."

"Don't believe all that you've heard," answered Fred modestly, "but I like football and have tried to do my best."

Fred was shocked when he reached home and found his father, pale and weak, seated by the fire. He shook hands with his father, but noted that his father's grasp was very weak. "I'm sorry you are ill," he said.

"Oh, I'll be all right, Fred," his father replied. "Now sit down and tell me about playing football at Yale. Your mother and I have been very proud of you."

After Fred found out about his father's illness, he decided to stay at home rather than return to Yale. He wanted to be with his father and felt that he should help his mother in this time of trouble. Only a few weeks later his father died.

Shortly after Colonel Remington's death, Mrs. Remington and Fred moved back to Canton. Walter Van Valkenburg also moved back with the horses and bought the Sackrider house beside the St. Lawrence County Fairground. In later years whenever Fred returned to Canton, he always went to see Van Valkenburg and his horses.

Exploring the
Great West

FOR A YEAR and a half after Colonel Remington died, Fred worked at a number of jobs, but all the while he was restless and eager for excitement. His father had left him a small inheritance and he decided to spend the money exploring the West. He looked upon the West as a land of enchantment and opportunity. From time to time he had heard of persons who had won fortunes in the West and he hoped that he, too, could win a fortune there.

Finally he discussed the matter with his mother, and she reluctantly consented to let him go. He made careful plans for his trip and in the summer of 1881 he took off for Montana. There he hoped to visit the battlefield near the Little Big Horn River where General Custer and his men had fallen. Afterwards he would explore other parts of the West.

Young Remington traveled by railroad and made his first stop at St. Paul, Minnesota. There he began to feel the throbbing of western life as he watched chugging steamboats on the Mississippi River and listened to the blasts of steam whistles at busy railroad stations. Already the West seemed to be alive.

At St. Paul Remington boarded a train for Miles City, Montana. The locomotive up front belched forth great clouds of black smoke and the train started its long journey. On the way out of the city, it passed long lines of freight cars waiting on the sidings.

As the train rushed westward, Remington watched out the windows with great interest. He looked out on miles and miles of open country, covered with grass and trees. Now and then when the train stopped at a railroad station, he saw people dressed in frontier clothes. Many of them were riding or driving horses.

The next day the train arrived at Miles City, which was the end of the line. The city was still more than a hundred miles from the Custer battlefield. From there Remington found that he could travel by stagecoach to Billings, about half the distance away.

While he was waiting in Miles City, he decided to purchase a western outfit and get rid of his eastern clothes. He entered a shop and purchased a complete outfit, including heavy duck trousers and jacket, a pair of riding boots, and a sombrero. After he left the shop, he splashed dirty water on the outfit to destroy its appearance of newness. Now he was happy because he looked like a man of the frontier.

Early the next morning he climbed aboard a stagecoach bound for Billings. All the way, as the stagecoach bumped and joggled slowly along, he looked out on the wild and desolate country. He was eager to reach Billings to find out what the West was really like.

When the stagecoach finally arrived, young Remington found the town alive with activity. He roamed about the few streets, enjoying the strange sights and sounds. He came across many cowboys and Indians and was fascinated by their costumes and their activities. Particularly he noticed the horses and ponies, which seemed to be everywhere.

Everything he saw, the people, the horses, the wooden buildings, the dusty streets, the vast rolling grassland stretching beyond the edges of the town, delighted him. For years he had dreamed of this land, and now he was seeing it in all its rough, raw, violent beauty. He

172

grinned with pleasure. "This is it!" he said to himself. "At last I'm seeing it!"

Remington spent several days in Billings, taking in the sights. During this time he visited several stables, hoping to buy a horse to ride on to the battlefield. Finally he bought a spirited bay mare and equipped her with a new saddle. Then he purchased some blankets and food and took off for the Little Big Horn River.

When he reached the battlefield, he found a cluster of white crosses at the top of a hill where General Custer and a few of his men had made their last stand. Other crosses round about marked where the other soldiers had fallen. Altogether there were more than two hundred crosses on the field.

As Remington looked at these crosses, he tried to imagine what had happened. General Custer and his men had gathered at the top of this hill overlooking the Little Big Horn River. Then

174

they had been surprised by several thousand Sioux Indians under the leadership of Chief Sitting Bull and his war chief Crazy Horse. The Indians had come out of hiding and had ridden round and round the hill, shouting and firing their rifles at Custer and his men. Finally they had completely overwhelmed the small trapped force and had killed every man.

At first Remington was overwhelmed by thoughts of the great tragedy that had happened here. Then his eyes glowed as he thought of the battle as a fine subject for a painting. Someday, after he learned more about Indians and soldiers in the West, he resolved to make a painting of this unfortunate battle.

After Remington left the battlefield, he proceeded to wander through other parts of the West, including Montana, Wyoming, the Dakotas, Nebraska, Colorado, and Kansas. As he roamed about, he tried to get acquainted with people, whether they were cowboys, trappers, or Indians. He worked as a cowboy, rode horseback to protect wagon trains, and hunted and spent time around campfires with Indians. He even took part in making attacks on renegade gangs of frontiersmen and Indians.

Everywhere Remington went he promptly adopted the ways of the people, and everywhere he went he made sketches of people in their typical costumes and surroundings. All the while he continued to make sketches of horses. In time he came to know the West almost as well as he had known his home town of Canton.

Finally in his travels through the West Remington reached Kansas City, a thriving city on the frontier. With money left from his father's estate, he purchased a ranch a few miles from the city. Here he decided to settle down for a while, but a year or so later he sold the ranch at almost a complete loss.

176

After Remington sold his ranch, he made an expedition to the Southwest to make sketches of cowboys, Indians, and horses. This was the one part of the West that he felt he knew the least about. Within a few months he returned to Kansas City with a fine collection of sketches and drawings based on this area.

In Kansas City Remington rented a little house and tried to sell some of his drawings. He disposed of a few drawings, but soon found that there was little demand for artwork in this frontier city. Even so, he refused to give up and was determined to keep on trying.

In the fall of 1884, Remington returned to the East to marry Eva Caten from Gloversville, New York, whom he had met before he had left for the West. He immediately took his bride, whom he called "Missie," to Kansas City to live. They settled in his little rented house, and once more he renewed his efforts to sell.

In the spring of 1885, one of Remington's drawings was used on the cover of *Harper's Weekly,* a popular national magazine. This drawing had been revised somewhat by a magazine artist, but it served to attract attention to Remington as an artist. He felt encouraged, but success still seemed to be a long way off.

In the meantime Remington failed to sell enough drawings and paintings to make a living for himself and "Missie." Finally, they decided that she should return to Gloversville to live with her parents. For a while, Remington would continue to explore and make sketches of the West. Then later he would return to the East, where he hoped to find a greater market for his paintings and drawings.

Remington immediately took off for Arizona, where the United States Army was trying to prevent an uprising among the Apache Indians. There he had an opportunity to sketch both cavalrymen and Indians in western costumes and surroundings. Particularly he was pleased to make sketches of broncos, burros, and mules, which belonged to the Indians. From Arizona, he went to Texas where he mingled with the Comanche Indians, who were noted for raising fine horses.

At the end of the summer Remington returned to Kansas City with a portfolio filled with sketches and drawings. Now at last he was ready to pass up the colorful wild West and head eastward to seek his fortune.

A Famous Artist

WHEN REMINGTON returned to the East, he headed for New York City with hundreds of sketches and drawings and only $3.00 in his pockets. His wife "Missie" came down from Gloversville to join him, and they arranged to stay temporarily with friends in Brooklyn.

At once Remington began to plod through the streets of New York, trying to sell his western sketches and drawings to magazines and book companies. He had to walk, because he was too poor to ride on horse-drawn street cars or to hire horse-drawn cabs. Walking was his only means of reaching places in the city.

At first he found little interest in his western pictures, but he kept on trying to sell them. Finally in 1886 *Harper's Weekly* used one of his Apache drawings on its cover. That same year he discovered that Poultney Bigelow, his old classmate at Yale, was editor of a magazine called *Outing*. Through Bigelow he obtained assignments to illustrate several western stories soon to be published.

During the next couple of years Remington became firmly established as an artist. A few of his paintings won top awards at national art exhibits. He began to receive numerous requests from publishers to illustrate numerous magazine articles and books. In 1888 he had fifty-four of his drawings reproduced in *Harper's Weekly*, thirty-two in *Outing*, sixty-four in *Century Magazine*, and twenty-seven in *Youth's Companion*. He no longer had to walk the streets to sell his artwork. Now the publishers were seeking him.

Some of the illustrations which Remington provided for *Century Magazine* were included in a series of articles written by Theodore Roosevelt, who had recently spent a few years in the West. Later this series of articles, including Remington's drawings, was published in a book called *Ranch Life and the Hunting Trail*. At this time Remington and Roosevelt became very close friends and from time to time later had many pleasant associations.

During these successful years Remington was a tireless worker. He arose regularly at six o'clock each morning and worked steadily until mid-afternoon. Then he would manage to get physical exercise by taking a long walk or riding horseback through a park. Some of his acquaintances said that he was the most vigorous and the busiest artist in America.

Now that Remington had a steady income, he and "Missie" moved to quarters of their own in

New York. Their new quarters were much nearer the publishing companies and enabled him to have a studio of his own. He decorated his studio with cowboy and Indian mementos, including costumes, saddles, guns, and curios which he had collected in his travels.

In 1889 Remington entered one of his paintings, "The Last Stand," in the exhibit of the Universal Exposition which was held in Paris, France. This exhibit included paintings and drawings by artists in many parts of the world. Remington won a silver medal for submitting the painting, which today is recognized as a classic. It shows General Custer and his men fighting their last bitter battle on the hill overlooking the Little Big Horn River.

In 1890 Remington was selected to provide artwork for an illustrated edition of the famous poem *The Song of Hiawatha* by Henry Wadsworth Longfellow. This artwork included twenty-two full-page drawings and nearly four hundred smaller drawings. By now Remington's name, although he was less than thirty years old, was fast becoming a household word in America.

Nearly every year Remington made a trip to some part of the West. In December, 1890, he visited the Badlands of South Dakota, which were swarming with hostile Sioux Indians. The Indians were angry because their leader, Sitting Bull, had just been killed by United States Army forces under General Nelson A. Miles.

Remington joined a scouting expedition and traveled among the hostile Indians. Soon after he returned east, the United States Army conquered the hostile Sioux Indians and ended the Indian wars. Immediately Remington wrote and illustrated a popular series of articles, called "The Sioux Outbreak in South Dakota," published in *Harper's Weekly*.

In 1892, Remington, now a highly successful

artist, purchased an estate with a large house and stable in New Rochelle, just north of New York City. Here he built a large studio with a skylight in the roof. At the back he built big double doors, wide enough to bring live horses in for models. He decorated the walls of the studio with all sorts of western mementos, including guns, swords, saddles, Indian costumes, tomahawks, and bows and arrows.

In the early nineties Remington and his former classmate at Yale, Poultney Bigelow, made a trip to Africa and Europe. This was a writing-drawing expedition with Poultney doing the writing and Remington doing the drawing. They traveled across northern Africa, where Remington made many sketches of Arabian horses.

From Africa they planned to travel in canoes up the Volga River in Russia, but the Russians objected to their writing and drawing and they had to leave. From Russia they went to Germany, where they visited the royal hunting lodge of Kaiser William, the ruler of Germany. Next they went to England, where they found Buffalo Bill's Wild West Show playing in London. Remington enjoyed this American show more than anything else he saw on the trip.

This same year Remington illustrated a book entitled *The Oregon Trail*, written by the famous historian Francis Parkman. The author selected Remington because he considered him the best American artist on western scenes. He wanted an artist who could make the West come alive.

Every now and then Remington made a trip to Mexico. He liked the wide-open country of Mexico, with its cowboys, Indians, and cattle. He wrote and illustrated several articles on Mexico, published in *Harper's Weekly*.

In 1895 Remington published his first book, *Pony Trails*. This book included fifteen of the best articles which he had written and illustrated for *Harper's Weekly.* Today this once-popular book is valuable as a collector's item.

In 1895 Remington became interested in sculpturing and produced his first sculpture, called "The Bronco Buster." This statue of a cowboy attempting to ride a wild horse was immediately accepted as a great work of art. Bronze copies were made and it soon became popular throughout the world.

Through succeeding years Remington produced twenty-four additional pieces of sculpture which were moulded in bronze. His "The Wicked Pony" shows a pony which has just thrown its rider to the ground. His "The Mountain Man" shows a horse and rider coming down a steep incline. His "The Outlaw" shows a horse that cannot be brought under control. His "Coming through the Rye" shows four cowboys riding broncos at full gallop and waving their guns.

In 1898, at the outbreak of the Spanish-

American War, Remington dashed off on assignment as both artist and reporter. He traveled with the United States Army in its attack on Cuba. He was present when his friend Theodore Roosevelt led the famous Rough Riders up San Juan Hill to capture the Spanish stronghold.

Later he made a famous painting, called "Charge of the Rough Riders at San Juan Hill." This painting shows Roosevelt leading the Rough Riders to a dramatic victory. It was used later with Roosevelt's own published story of this dramatic battle.

All through his busy years as an artist and sculptor, he made frequent vacation trips to Canton and the North Country. In 1898 he purchased an island, called "Ingleneuk," in the St. Lawrence River, which belonged to the North Country. He remodeled and enlarged the house and built a large studio on the island. Here he and "Missie" spent about three months each

summer, fishing, paddling his Rushton canoe, and entertaining friends.

During these years Remington kept up his painting and sculpturing and wrote many magazine articles and books on the West. His friend Theodore Roosevelt encouraged him to write as well as to paint. In one period of five years soon after the turn of the century Remington wrote six different books.

In his later years Remington prepared many paintings for *Collier's Weekly*. In 1905 this magazine devoted a complete issue of the magazine, called the "Remington Number," to Remington and his work. Remington now reached the pinnacle of his career.

In 1908, Remington and "Missie" decided to purchase a small farm in Ridgefield, Connecticut. Here they built a large house, an elaborate studio, and a stable, all of which he called "Remington Village." The following spring they moved from New Rochelle to this new home, but unfortunately Remington had little opportunity to enjoy it. In December of that same year he became suddenly ill and died.

Remington's sudden death came as a great shock to the country. Many of his paintings and drawings and many of his articles and books were republished. Then gradually his paintings, drawings, sculptures, articles, and books were assembled in four great art museums of the country, one in Ogdensburg, New York, and the others in the West and South. Altogether he produced 2,739 paintings and drawings.

In 1940 the United States government issued a commemorative bronze two-cent stamp in Remington's honor. In 1961 it issued another commemorative stamp to honor him on the centennial of his birth. Numerous art societies and organizations have repeatedly paid tribute to him for his extensive contributions to American art.

Few artists have possessed Remington's amazing ability to wield a pencil, pen, brush, or scalpel. Back of this amazing skill was his remarkable photographic memory. He saw everything and could store away for future use the smallest details of what he saw.

Frederic Remington will always be revered for helping to preserve the great West in vivid drawings, paintings, sculptures, and writings. He lived for a time in the West and knew it as it really was. Furthermore, he possessed the rare ability to make it come alive.

More About This Book

WHEN FREDERIC REMINGTON LIVED

1861   FREDERIC REMINGTON WAS BORN IN CANTON, NEW YORK, OCTOBER 4.

There were thirty-four states in the Union.

Abraham Lincoln was President.

The population of the country was about 32,150,000.

1861–   FRED LIVED AND ATTENDED SCHOOL IN CAN-
1875   TON AND OGDENSBURG, NEW YORK.

The War between the States was fought, 1861–1865.

President Lincoln was assassinated and Andrew Johnson became President, 1865.

The first transcontinental railroad was completed, 1869.

Montgomery Ward and Company, first mail order house in America, was founded, 1872.

The first arch bridge across the Mississippi River was completed at St. Louis, 1874.

193

Alexander Graham Bell invented the telephone, 1876.

General George Custer's army was massacred in Montana, 1876.

Thomas A. Edison invented the phonograph, 1878, and the electric light, 1879.

James A. Garfield became President and was assassinated, 1881.

The Equal Rights Party was formed to promote the rights of women, 1884.

The Washington Monument in Washington, D.C. was dedicated, 1885.

Thomas A. Edison invented the moving-picture camera, 1889.

Henry Ford built his first automobile, 1896.

Wilbur and Orville Wright flew the first heavier-than-air aircraft, 1903.

194

1909 FREDERIC REMINGTON DIED IN RIDGEFIELD,
CONNECTICUT, DECEMBER 29.

There were forty-six states in the Union.

William Howard Taft was President.

The population of the country was about
90,375,000.

DO YOU REMEMBER?

1. How did Fred come to learn much about horses
while he was still a small boy?

2. How did Fred demonstrate during his early years
that he liked to draw?

3. How did Fred help to fight the fire that destroyed
the *Plaindealer* office?

4. What did Fred and his friends see and do at the
St. Lawrence County Fair?

5. How did Fred and his friends enjoy the area
around Canton, known as the North Country?

6. How did Fred and his friends put in an exciting
day at the circus?

7. How did Fred continue to keep up his interest in
drawing horses?

8. Why did Fred and Pete fail to enjoy swimming in Grass River?

9. Why did the Remington family move from Canton, New York, to Ogdensburg, New York?

10. What different schools did Fred attend away from home as he was growing up?

11. How did young Remington accumulate a collection of realistic sketches of the West?

12. How did Remington, noted for his Western drawings and paintings, become a famous artist?

13. How did Remington, later in life, become noted for writing and sculpturing?

14. What are the names of some of Remington's most famous paintings and statues?

IT'S FUN TO LOOK UP THESE THINGS

1. Why was the North Country, where Frederic Remington grew up, a very scenic area?

2. What were some of the leading ranching areas when Remington first visited the West?

3. What were some of the leading Indian tribes in the West at that time?

4. Why were many United States cavalrymen stationed in different parts of the West?
5. What states were still territories when Remington visited the West?
6. What important magazines were published in New York prior to the turn of the century?

INTERESTING THINGS YOU CAN DO

1. Draw a map of New York state to show where Canton and Ogdensburg were located.
2. Make a list of important western settlements when Remington explored the West.
3. Collect pictures to show what the West was like at the time of Remington's visits.
4. Make a copy of one of Remington's famous paintings to place on the bulletin board.
5. Explain the difference between realistic art and imaginative art.
6. Name other important American artists with some of their famous paintings.
7. Name other important American sculptors with some of their famous statues.

OTHER BOOKS YOU MAY ENJOY READING

Benjamin West: Gifted Young Painter, Dorothea J. Snow. Trade and School Editions, Bobbs-Merrill.

Big Book of Cowboys, Sydney E. Fletcher. Grosset.

Cowboys and Cattle Country, by the editors of American Heritage. Meredith.

George Custer: Boy of Action, Augusta Stevenson. Trade and School Editions, Bobbs-Merrill.

Indians of the Plains, Eugene Rachlis and John C. Ewers. Harper and Row.

Painter of the Wild West: Frederic Remington, Robin McKown. Messner.

INTERESTING WORDS IN THIS BOOK

astonished (ăs tŏn'ĭsht) : surprised, amazed

bay (bā) : reddish-brown

brigade (brĭ gād') : group of persons organized for a specific purpose

cavity (kăv'ĭ tĭ) : hole, hollow place

classification (klăs'ĭ fĭ kā'shŭn) : systematic arrangement, grouping according to a plan

climax (klī'măks) : highest point of interest

commemorative (kŏ mĕm'ô rā'tĭv) : meant to preserve the memory of

curio (kū'rĭ ō) : any article valued as a curiosity

enthusiasm (ĕn thū'zĭ ăz'm) : eager interest

excavation (ĕks'kȧ vā'shŭn) : hole made by digging

flexibility (flĕk'sĭ bĭl'ĭ tĭ) : state of being easily bent

gallant (găl'ănt) : noble and brave

grade (grād) : make level, smooth out

hilt (hĭlt) : handle

mammoth (măm'ŭth) : very large

meritorious (mĕr'ĭ tō'rĭ ŭs) : worthy of praise or reward, deserving

oval (ō'văl) : egg-shaped

portfolio (pôrt fō'lĭ ō) : case for carrying drawings or loose papers

premium (prē'mĭ ŭm) : award, prize

pun (pŭn) : humorous play on words that sound alike but have different meanings

quarter horse (kwôr'tĕr hôrs) : horse trained to run at great speed for short distances, usually a quarter of a mile

rapt (răpt) : completely engrossed or absorbed

rhythmic (rĭth′mĭk) : having to do with rhythm or a regular repetition of accent or beat

robust (rȯ bŭst′) : strong, vigorous

saunter (sôn′tēr) : wander about aimlessly

skeptical (skĕp′tĭ kăl) : doubting, questioning, hard to convince

sociable (sō′shă b′l) : friendly with others

sorrel (sŏr′ĕl) : brown, yellow-red color

stilted (stĭl′tĕd) : formal and dignified

submerged (sŭb mûrjd′) : flooded, covered with water

sumac (sū′măk) : small shrub or tree, sometimes poisonous, noted for beautiful red berries and leaves in the fall

surrey (sûr′ĭ) : carriage with four wheels and two seats

technique (tĕk nēk′) : method or way of doing something

temperament (tĕm′pēr *a* mĕnt) : make-up or disposition of a person

tongs (tôngz) : two-handled instrument for taking hot objects from a fire

unison (ū′nĭ *sŭn*) : agreement

wisecrack (wīz′krăk) : smart or joking remark

yoke (yōk) : team, pair

Childhood
OF FAMOUS AMERICANS

CHILDHOOD OF FAMOUS AMERICANS

THE NATION DIVIDED

ABE LINCOLN, *Stevenson*
ABNER DOUBLEDAY, *Dunham*
BEDFORD FORREST, *Parks*
CLARA BARTON, *Stevenson*
DAVID FARRAGUT, *Long*
HARRIET BEECHER STOWE, *Widdemer*
JEB STUART, *Winders*
JEFF DAVIS, *de Grummond and Delaune*
JULIA WARD HOWE, *Wagoner*
MARY TODD LINCOLN, *Wilkie*
RAPHAEL SEMMES, *Snow*
ROBERT E. LEE, *Monsell*
TOM JACKSON, *Monsell*
U. S. GRANT, *Stevenson*

RECONSTRUCTION and EXPANSION

ALECK BELL, *Widdemer*
ALLAN PINKERTON, *Borland and Speicher*
ANDREW CARNEGIE, *Henry*
BOOKER T. WASHINGTON, *Stevenson*
CHIEF JOSEPH, *Burt*
CYRUS McCORMICK, *Dobler*
DOROTHEA DIX, *Melin*
EUGENE FIELD, *Borland and Speicher*
FRANCES WILLARD, *Mason*
GEORGE CUSTER, *Stevenson*
GEORGE PULLMAN, *Myers*
HENRY WADSWORTH LONGFELLOW, *Melin*
JOEL CHANDLER HARRIS, *Weddle*
JOHN DEERE, *Bare*
JOHN WANAMAKER, *Burt*
LEW WALLACE, *Schaaf*
LOUISA ALCOTT, *Wagoner*
LUTHER BURBANK, *Burt* ·
MARIA MITCHELL, *Melin*
MARK TWAIN, *Mason*
MARY MAPES DODGE, *Mason*
P. T. BARNUM, *Stevenson*
ROBERT TODD LINCOLN, *Anderson*
SITTING BULL, *Stevenson*
SUSAN ANTHONY, *Monsell*
TOM EDISON, *Guthridge*

TURN of the CENTURY

ANNIE OAKLEY, *Wilson*
DAN BEARD, *Mason*
ELIZABETH BLACKWELL, *Henry*
F. W. WOOLWORTH, *Myers*
GEORGE CARVER, *Stevenson*
GEORGE DEWEY, *Long*
GEORGE EASTMAN, *Henry*
GEORGE WESTINGHOUSE, *Dunham*
J. STERLING MORTON, *Moore*
JAMES WHITCOMB RILEY, *Mitchell*

JANE ADDAMS, *Wagoner*
JOHN BURROUGHS, *Frisbee*
JOHN PHILIP SOUSA, *Weil*
JULIETTE LOW, *Higgins*
KATE DOUGLAS WIGGIN, *Mason*
KATHARINE LEE BATES, *Myers*
LILIUOKALANI, *Newman*
THE RINGLING BROTHERS, *Burt*
ROBERT PEARY, *Clark*
TEDDY ROOSEVELT, *Parks*
WALTER REED, *Higgins*
WILBUR AND ORVILLE WRIGHT, *Stevenson*
WILL AND CHARLIE MAYO, *Hammontree*

IN RECENT YEARS

ADLAI STEVENSON, *Ward*
ALBERT EINSTEIN, *Hammontree*
ALVIN C. YORK, *Weddle*
AMELIA EARHART, *Howe*
A. P. GIANNINI, *Hammontree*
BABE DIDRIKSON, *de Grummond and Delaune*
BABE RUTH, *Van Riper, Jr.*
CARL BEN EIELSON, *Myers and Burnett*
CECIL B. DeMILLE, *Myers and Burnett*
CLYDE BEATTY, *Wilkie*
DOUGLAS MACARTHUR, *Long*
EDWARD BOK, *Myers*
EDWARD R. MURROW, *Myers and Burnett*
ELEANOR ROOSEVELT, *Weil*
ERNIE PYLE, *Wilson*
ETHEL BARRYMORE, *Newman*
FRANKLIN ROOSEVELT, *Weil*
GEORGE GERSHWIN, *Bryant*
GEORGE M. COHAN *Winders*
GLENN L. MARTIN, *Harley*
HARVEY S. FIRESTONE, *Paradis*
HELEN KELLER, *Wilkie*
HENRY FORD, *Aird and Ruddiman*
HERBERT HOOVER, *Comfort*
JEAN FELIX PICCARD, *de Grummond and Delaune*
JIM THORPE, *Van Riper, Jr.*
JOHN F. KENNEDY, *Frisbee*
KNUTE ROCKNE, *Van Riper, Jr.*
LEE DeFOREST, *Dobler*
LOU GEHRIG, *Van Riper, Jr.*
MARTIN LUTHER KING, JR., *Millender*
OLIVER WENDELL HOLMES, JR., *Dunham*
RICHARD BYRD, *Van Riper, Jr.*
ROBERT FROST, *Wilson*
ROBERT GODDARD, *Moore*
VILHJALMUR STEFANSSON, *Myers and Burnett*
WALT DISNEY, *Hammontree*
WALTER CHRYSLER, *Weddle*
WILL ROGERS, *Van Riper, Jr.*
WOODROW WILSON, *Monsell*